CGP has National 5 Biology covered!

This CGP book is the best way to revise for SQA National 5 Biology — no contest. We've explained everything you need to know in a chatty style that's easy to understand.

There's also a serving of exam-style questions to test you on what you've learned, plus a few daft jokes to keep you motivated. Why bother with anyone else's dull book?

How to access your free Online Edition

This book includes a free Online Edition to read on your PC, Mac or tablet. To access it, just go to **cgpbooks.co.uk/extras** and enter this code...

2021 9757 1895 1742

By the way, this code only works for one person. If somebody else has used this book before you, they might have already claimed the Online Edition.

CGP — the best by miles! ☺

Our sole aim here at CGP is to produce the highest quality books — carefully written, immaculately presented and dangerously close to being funny.

Then we work our socks off to get them out to you — at the cheapest possible prices.

Contents

Published by CGP

From original material by Richard Parsons

Editors: Luke Bennett, Daniel Fielding, Sarah Pattison, Rachael Rogers and Camilla Simson
Contributors: Kirstie Carvalho and Paddy Gannon

ISBN: 978 1 78294 991 6

With thanks to Phil Armstrong, Ellen Burton and Hayley Thompson for the proofreading.
With thanks to Jan Greenway for the copyright research.

Printed by Elanders Ltd, Newcastle upon Tyne.
Clipart from Corel®

The Scientific Method

This section <u>isn't</u> about how to 'do' science — but it does show you the way <u>most scientists</u> work.

Scientists Come Up With Hypotheses — Then Test Them

1) Scientists try to <u>explain</u> things. They start by <u>observing</u> something they don't understand.

2) They then come up with a <u>hypothesis</u> — a possible <u>explanation</u> for what they've observed.

3) The next step is to <u>test</u> whether the hypothesis might be <u>right or not</u>. This involves making a <u>prediction</u> based on the hypothesis and testing it by <u>gathering evidence</u> (i.e. <u>data</u>) from <u>investigations</u>. If <u>evidence</u> from <u>experiments</u> backs up a prediction, you're a step closer to figuring out if the hypothesis is true.

Hundreds of years ago, we thought demons caused illness.

Several Scientists Will Test a Hypothesis

1) Normally, scientists <u>share</u> their <u>findings</u> in <u>peer-reviewed journals</u>, or at <u>conferences</u>.

2) <u>Peer-review</u> is where <u>other scientists</u> check results and scientific explanations to make sure they're 'scientific' (e.g. that experiments have been done in a sensible way) <u>before</u> they're published. It helps to <u>detect false claims</u>, but it doesn't mean that findings are <u>correct</u> — just that they're not wrong in any <u>obvious</u> way.

3) Once other scientists have found out about a hypothesis, they'll start basing their <u>own predictions</u> on it and carry out their <u>own experiments</u>. They'll also try to <u>reproduce</u> the original experiments to <u>check the results</u> — and if all the experiments in the world <u>back up</u> the <u>hypothesis</u>, then scientists start to think the hypothesis is <u>true</u>.

4) However, if a scientist does an experiment that <u>doesn't fit</u> with the hypothesis (and other scientists can reproduce the results) then the hypothesis may need to be <u>modified</u> or <u>scrapped</u> altogether.

Then we thought it was caused by 'bad blood' (and treated it with leeches).

If All the Evidence Supports a Hypothesis, It's Accepted — For Now

1) <u>Accepted hypotheses</u> are often referred to as <u>theories</u>. Our <u>currently accepted</u> theories are the ones that have survived this 'trial by evidence' — they've been <u>tested many times</u> over the years and <u>survived</u>.

2) However, theories <u>never</u> become totally indisputable <u>fact</u>. If <u>new evidence</u> comes along that <u>can't be explained</u> using the existing theory, then the hypothesising and testing is likely to <u>start all over again</u>.

Now we've collected more evidence, we know that illnesses that can be spread between people are due to microorganisms.

Theories Can Involve Different Types of Models

1) A <u>representational model</u> is a <u>simplified description</u> or <u>picture</u> of what's going on in real life. Like all models, it can be used to <u>explain observations</u> and <u>make predictions</u>. E.g. enzyme action can be <u>modelled</u> by thinking about the joining together of the enzyme active site and the substrate in terms of their <u>complementary shapes</u> (see p.24). This model can be used to <u>explain</u> why enzymes only catalyse particular reactions.

Scientists test models by carrying out experiments to check that the predictions made by the model happen as expected.

2) <u>Computational models</u> use computers to make <u>simulations</u> of complex real-life processes, such as climate change. They're used when there are a <u>lot</u> of different <u>variables</u> (factors that change) to consider, and because you can easily <u>change their design</u> to take into account <u>new data</u>.

3) All models have <u>limitations</u> on what they can <u>explain</u> or <u>predict</u>. Climate change models have several limitations — for example, it's hard to take into account all the biological and chemical processes that influence climate. It can also be difficult to include regional variations in climate.

I'm off to the zoo to test my hippo-thesis...

The scientific method has developed over time, and many people have helped to develop it. From Aristotle to modern day scientists, lots of people have contributed. And many more are likely to contribute in the future.

Communication & Issues Created by Science

Scientific developments can be great, but they can sometimes <u>raise more questions</u> than they answer...

It's Important to Communicate Scientific Discoveries to the General Public

Some scientific discoveries show that people should <u>change their habits</u>, or they might provide ideas that could be <u>developed</u> into new <u>technology</u>. So scientists need to <u>tell the world</u> about their discoveries.

> <u>Gene technologies</u> are used in <u>genetic engineering</u> to produce <u>genetically modified crops</u> (see p.26). Information about these crops needs to be communicated to <u>farmers</u> who might <u>benefit</u> from growing them and to the <u>general public</u>, so they can make <u>informed decisions</u> about the food they buy and eat.

Scientific Evidence can be Presented in a Biased Way

1) <u>Reports</u> about scientific discoveries in the <u>media</u> (e.g. newspapers or television) <u>aren't</u> peer-reviewed.

2) This means that, even though news stories are often <u>based</u> on data that has been peer-reviewed, the data might be <u>presented</u> in a way that is <u>over-simplified</u> or <u>inaccurate</u>, making it open to <u>misinterpretation</u>.

3) People who want to make a point can sometimes <u>present data</u> in a <u>biased way</u>. (Sometimes <u>without knowing</u> they're doing it.) For example, a scientist might overemphasise a relationship in the data, or a newspaper article might describe details of data <u>supporting</u> an idea without giving any evidence <u>against</u> it.

Scientific Developments are Great, but they can Raise Issues

Scientific <u>knowledge is increased</u> by doing experiments. And this knowledge leads to <u>scientific developments</u>, e.g. new technologies or new advice. These developments can create <u>issues</u> though. For example:

<u>Economic issues:</u> Society <u>can't</u> always <u>afford</u> to do things scientists recommend (e.g. investing in alternative energy sources) without <u>cutting back elsewhere</u>.

<u>Social issues:</u> Decisions based on scientific evidence affect <u>people</u> — e.g. should alcohol be banned (to prevent health problems)? Would the <u>effect on people's lifestyles be acceptable...?</u>

<u>Personal issues:</u> Some decisions will affect <u>individuals</u>. For example, someone might support <u>alternative energy</u>, but object if a <u>wind farm</u> is built next to their house.

<u>Environmental issues:</u> <u>Human activity</u> often affects the <u>natural environment</u> — e.g. <u>genetically modified crops</u> may help us to produce <u>more food</u> — but some people think they could cause <u>environmental problems</u>.

Science Can't Answer Every Question — Especially Ethical Ones

1) We don't <u>understand everything</u>. We're always finding out <u>more</u>, but we'll never know <u>all</u> the answers.

2) In order to answer scientific questions, scientists need <u>data</u> to provide <u>evidence</u> for their hypotheses.

3) Some questions can't be answered <u>yet</u> because the data <u>can't</u> currently be <u>collected</u>, or because there's <u>not enough</u> data to <u>support</u> a theory.

4) <u>Eventually</u>, as we get <u>more evidence</u>, we'll answer some of the questions that <u>currently</u> can't be answered, e.g. what the impact of global warming on sea levels will be. But there will always be the "<u>Should we be doing this at all?</u>"-type questions that experiments <u>can't</u> help us to answer...

> Think about <u>new drugs which can be taken to boost your 'brain power'</u>.
> - Some people think they're <u>good</u> as they could improve concentration or memory. New drugs could let people think in ways beyond the powers of normal brains.
> - Other people say they're <u>bad</u> — they could give you an <u>unfair advantage</u> in exams. And people might be <u>pressured</u> into taking them so that they could work more <u>effectively</u>, and for <u>longer hours</u>.

Tea to milk or milk to tea? — Totally unanswerable by science...

Science can't tell you whether or not you should do something. That's for you and society to decide. But there are tons of questions science might be able to answer, like where life came from and where my superhero socks are.

Designing Investigations

Dig out your lab coat and dust down your badly-scratched safety goggles... it's <u>investigation time</u>. You need to know how to <u>plan</u> and <u>carry out</u> investigations. But before we get into the ins and outs of what makes a good experiment, let's talk about <u>safety</u>...

Investigations Can be Hazardous

Investigations include experiments and studies.

1) A <u>hazard</u> is something that could <u>potentially cause harm</u>.

2) Hazards from <u>science experiments</u> might include:

- <u>Microorganisms</u>, e.g. some bacteria can make you ill.
- <u>Chemicals</u>, e.g. sulfuric acid can burn your skin and alcohols catch fire easily.
- <u>Fire</u>, e.g. an unattended Bunsen burner is a fire hazard.
- <u>Electricity</u>, e.g. faulty electrical equipment could give you a shock.

Hmm... Where did my bacteria sample go?

3) Part of planning an investigation is making sure that it's <u>safe</u>.

4) You should always make sure that you <u>identify</u> all the hazards that you might encounter. Then you should think of ways of <u>reducing the risks</u> from the hazards you've identified. For example:

- If you're working with <u>sulfuric acid</u>, always wear gloves and safety goggles. This will reduce the risk of the acid coming into contact with your skin and eyes.
- If you're using a <u>Bunsen burner</u>, stand it on a heat proof mat. This will reduce the risk of starting a fire.

You can find out about potential hazards by looking in textbooks, doing some internet research, or asking your teacher.

An Investigation Must Have an Aim

1) Before you begin <u>any</u> investigation, you need to have an <u>aim</u>.

2) An aim should <u>clearly describe</u> the <u>purpose</u> of your investigation. For example:

To investigate how wind speed affects the rate of transpiration in a plant.

Investigations Produce Evidence to Support or Disprove a Hypothesis

1) Scientists <u>observe</u> things and come up with <u>hypotheses</u> to explain them (see p.2). The investigations you do will be based on the same principle. For example:

<u>Observation</u>: People have big feet and spots. <u>Hypothesis</u>: Having big feet causes spots.

2) To <u>determine</u> whether or not a hypothesis is <u>right</u>, you need to do an <u>investigation</u> to gather evidence. To do this, you need to use the hypothesis to make a <u>prediction</u> — something you think <u>will happen</u> that you can <u>test</u>. E.g. people with bigger feet will have more spots.

3) Investigations are used to see if there are <u>patterns</u> or <u>relationships</u> between <u>two variables</u>, e.g. to see if there's a pattern or relationship between the variables 'number of spots' and 'size of feet'.

Evidence Needs to be Reliable and Valid

1) Data is <u>reliable</u> if it's <u>repeatable</u> and <u>reproducible</u>. Scientists are more likely to <u>have confidence</u> in reliable data.

2) <u>Repeatable</u> means that if the <u>same person</u> does an experiment again using the <u>same methods</u> and equipment, they'll get <u>similar results</u>.

3) <u>Reproducible</u> means that if <u>someone else</u> does the experiment, or a <u>different</u> method or piece of equipment is used, the results will still be <u>similar</u>.

4) <u>Valid results</u> are both repeatable and reproducible AND they <u>answer the original question</u>. They come from experiments that were designed to be a <u>fair test</u> (see next page).

Designing Investigations

Controlling Variables Improves Validity

1) A variable is something that has the potential to <u>change</u>, e.g. temperature.
   In a lab experiment you usually <u>change one variable</u> and <u>measure</u> how it affects <u>another variable</u>.

> <u>Example</u>: you might change <u>only</u> the temperature of an enzyme-controlled reaction and measure how it affects the rate of reaction.

2) To make it a <u>fair test</u>, <u>everything else</u> that could affect the results should <u>stay the same</u> — otherwise you can't tell if the thing you're changing is causing the results or not.

> <u>Example continued</u>: you need to keep the pH the same, otherwise you won't know if any change in the rate of reaction is caused by the change in temperature, or the change in pH.

Part of designing an investigation includes choosing the most appropriate apparatus and techniques to measure or control your variables — see pages 72-73.

3) The variable you <u>CHANGE</u> is called the <u>INDEPENDENT</u> variable.

4) The variable you <u>MEASURE</u> is called the <u>DEPENDENT</u> variable.

5) The variables that you <u>KEEP THE SAME</u> are called <u>CONTROL</u> variables.

> <u>Example continued</u>:
> Independent variable = temperature
> Dependent variable = rate of reaction
> Control variables = pH, volume of reactants, concentration of reactants, etc.

6) Because you can't always control all the variables, you often need to use a <u>CONTROL EXPERIMENT</u> — an experiment that's kept under the <u>same conditions</u> as the rest of the investigation, but doesn't have anything done to it. This is so that you can see what happens when you don't change anything at all.

The Bigger the Sample Size the Better

1) Data based on <u>small samples</u> isn't as good as data based on large samples.

2) A sample should <u>represent</u> the <u>whole population</u> (i.e. it should share as many of the characteristics in the population as possible) — a small sample can't do that as well. It's also harder to spot <u>anomalies</u> if your sample size is too small.

Anomalies are results that don't fit in with the rest — see next page.

3) The <u>bigger</u> the sample size the <u>better</u>, but scientists have to be <u>realistic</u> when choosing how big.

4) For example, if you were studying how lifestyle affects people's weight it'd be great to study everyone in the UK (a huge sample), but it'd take ages and cost a bomb. It's more realistic to study a thousand people, with a mixture of ages, gender and race.

Cake samples

This is no high street survey — it's a designer investigation...

Planning an investigation is tricky business — you need to make sure that you've thought of everything in order for your method to give you valid results. And, not only do you need to be able to plan your own investigations, you should also be able to look at someone else's plan and decide whether or not it needs improving. Remember, whoever's plan you're thinking about, always consider any potential hazar... oof, sorry, I tripped.

Collecting Data

You've designed the perfect investigation — now it's time to get your hands mucky and <u>collect some data</u>.

Your Data Should be Reliable, Accurate and Precise

1) <u>Reliable</u> results are <u>repeatable</u> and <u>reproducible</u>.

2) To <u>check repeatability</u> you need to <u>repeat</u> the readings and check that the results are similar. You need to repeat each reading at least <u>three times</u>.

Brian's result was a curate.

3) To make sure your results are <u>reproducible</u> you can cross check them by taking a <u>second set of readings</u> with <u>another instrument</u> (or a <u>different observer</u>).

4) Your data also needs to be ACCURATE. Really accurate results are those that are <u>really close</u> to the <u>true answer</u>. The accuracy of your results usually depends on your <u>method</u> — you need to make sure you're measuring the right thing and that you don't <u>miss anything</u> that should be included in the measurements. E.g. estimating the <u>amount of gas</u> released from a reaction by <u>counting the bubbles</u> isn't very accurate because you might <u>miss</u> some of the bubbles and they might have different <u>volumes</u>. It's <u>more accurate</u> to collect the gas and then determine its volume (see p.72).

5) Your data also needs to be PRECISE. Precise results are ones where the data is <u>all really close</u> to the <u>mean</u> (average) of your repeated results (i.e. not spread out).

Repeat	Data set 1	Data set 2
1	12	11
2	14	17
3	13	14
Mean	13	14

Data set 1 is more precise than data set 2.

Your Equipment has to be Right for the Job

1) The measuring equipment you use has to be <u>sensitive enough</u> to measure the changes you're looking for. For example, if you need to measure changes of 1 cm^3 you need to use a measuring cylinder that can measure in 1 cm^3 steps — it'd be no good trying with one that only measures in 10 cm^3 steps.

2) The <u>smallest change</u> a measuring instrument can <u>detect</u> is called its RESOLUTION. E.g. some mass balances have a resolution of 1 g, some have a resolution of 0.1 g, and some are even more sensitive.

3) Also, equipment needs to be <u>calibrated</u> by measuring a known value. If there's a <u>difference</u> between the <u>measured</u> and <u>known value</u>, you can use this to <u>correct</u> the inaccuracy of the equipment.

You Need to Look out for Errors and Anomalous Results

1) The results of your experiment will always <u>vary a bit</u> because of RANDOM ERRORS — unpredictable differences caused by things like <u>human errors</u> in <u>measuring</u>. E.g. the errors you make when reading from a measuring cylinder are random. You have to estimate or round the level when it's between two marks — so sometimes your figure will be a bit above the real one, and sometimes it will be a bit below.

2) You can <u>reduce</u> the effect of random errors by taking <u>repeat readings</u> and finding the <u>mean</u>. This will make your results <u>more precise</u>.

If there's no systematic error, then doing repeats and calculating a mean can make your results more accurate.

3) If a measurement is wrong by the <u>same amount every time</u>, it's called a SYSTEMATIC ERROR. For example, if you measured from the very end of your ruler instead of from the 0 cm mark every time, all your measurements would be a bit small. Repeating the experiment in the exact same way and calculating a mean <u>won't</u> correct a systematic error.

4) Just to make things more complicated, if a systematic error is caused by using <u>equipment</u> that <u>isn't zeroed properly</u>, it's called a ZERO ERROR. For example, if a mass balance always reads 1 gram before you put anything on it, all your measurements will be 1 gram too heavy.

5) You can <u>compensate</u> for some systematic errors if you know about them though, e.g. if your mass balance always reads 1 gram before you put anything on it you can subtract 1 gram from all your results.

6) Sometimes you get a result that <u>doesn't fit in</u> with the rest at all. This is called an ANOMALOUS RESULT. You should investigate it and try to <u>work out what happened</u>. If you can work out what happened (e.g. you measured something totally wrong) you can <u>ignore</u> it when processing your results.

Watch what you say to that mass balance — it's very sensitive...

Weirdly, data can be really precise but not very accurate. For example, a fancy piece of lab equipment might give results that are really precise, but if it's not been calibrated properly those results won't be accurate.

Processing Data

Once you've collected data you'll need to process it so it's easier to see what your results show.

Data Needs to be Organised

Tables are dead useful for organising data. When you draw a table use a ruler and make sure each column has a heading (including the units).

You Might Have to Find the Average

1) When you've done repeats of an experiment you should always calculate the mean (a type of average). To do this add together all the data values and divide by the total number of values in the sample.

EXAMPLE: The results of an experiment to find the volume of gas produced in an enzyme-controlled reaction are shown below. Calculate the mean volume.

Repeat 1 (cm³)	Repeat 2 (cm³)	Repeat 3 (cm³)	Mean (cm³)
28	37	32	(28 + 37 + 32) ÷ 3 = 32

Ignore anomalous results when calculating the mean.

2) You might also need to calculate the median or mode (two more types of average). To calculate the median, put all your data in numerical order — the median is the middle value. The number that appears most often in a data set is the mode.

If you have an even number of values, the median is halfway between the middle two values.

You Might Need to Calculate Percentages

A way of comparing quantities is to use percentages. If you want to give the amount X as a percentage of total amount Y, you do it like this:

$$\% = \frac{X}{Y} \times 100$$

EXAMPLE: A student counted 20 plants within a quadrat. She identified 6 of those plants as daisies. What percentage of the plants were daisies?

1) Divide 6 by 20.
2) Multiply this amount by 100.

1. 6 ÷ 20 = 0.3
2. 0.3 × 100 = 30% of the plants were daisies.

When investigating the change in a variable, you may want to compare results that didn't have the same initial value. You can do this by calculating the percentage change, like this:

$$\% \text{ change} = \frac{\text{final value} - \text{original value}}{\text{original value}} \times 100$$

EXAMPLE: To investigate osmosis, a student records the mass of potato cylinders before and after placing them in sugar solutions of different concentrations.

Which potato cylinder had the largest percentage change?

Potato cylinder	Concentration (mol/dm³)	Mass at start (g)	Mass at end (g)
1	0.0	7.5	8.7
2	1.0	8.0	6.8

1) Stick each set of results into the equation:

$$\% \text{ change} = \frac{\text{final value} - \text{original value}}{\text{original value}} \times 100$$

1. $\frac{8.7 - 7.5}{7.5} \times 100 = 16\%$

The mass at the start is the original value. The mass at the end is the final value.

2. $\frac{6.8 - 8.0}{8.0} \times 100 = -15\%$

Here, percentage change is negative, because the mass has decreased.

2) Compare the results. 16% is greater than 15%, so potato cylinder 1 had the largest percentage change.

My enjoyment of revision just decreased by 99%...

Knowing what to do with your data is really important — so important, in fact, that there's more about it coming up...

Processing and Presenting Data

Don't put your calculator away just yet, there's more <u>mathsy stuff</u> coming up. But then it's on to looking at how you can <u>present</u> your results in a nice <u>chart</u> or <u>graph</u> to help you <u>spot any patterns</u> in your data.

Ratios *Can be Used to Compare Results*

1) Ratios <u>compare two values</u> and are usually written like this: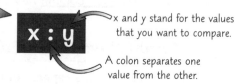

x and y stand for the values that you want to compare.

A colon separates one value from the other.

2) You need to write a ratio the <u>right way round</u> depending on what information you're trying to give. For example, if there are <u>200 dandelions</u> in a field and <u>600 buttercups</u>, the ratio of dandelions to buttercups is 200 : 600, but the ratio of buttercups to dandelions is 600 : 200.

3) Ratios are usually most useful when written as a <u>simple, whole number ratio</u>. To get a ratio in this form, divide each side by the <u>same number</u> until there's <u>nothing</u> left you can divide by to give <u>whole numbers</u>.

> **EXAMPLE:** Give the ratio 1.2 : 3.6 as a simple, whole number ratio.
> 1) To simplify the ratio 1.2 : 3.6, <u>divide both sides</u> by 1.2. $1.2 \div 1.2 = 1$
> 2) You can't divide 1 and 3 by the same number to get two whole numbers, so this must be the ratio's simplest form. $3.6 \div 1.2 = 3$
>   **1 : 3**

Be Aware of Significant Figures in Calculations

The <u>first significant figure</u> of a number is the first digit that's <u>not zero</u>.
The second and third significant figures come <u>straight after</u> (even if they're zeros).

1) For your final answer, you should round to the <u>lowest number of significant figures</u> (s.f.) given.
2) Remember to write down <u>how many</u> significant figures you've rounded to after your answer.
3) If your calculation has multiple steps, <u>only</u> round the <u>final</u> answer, or it won't be as accurate.

> **EXAMPLE:** A plant produces 10.2 cm³ of oxygen in 6.5 minutes whilst photosynthesising. Calculate the rate of photosynthesis.
> rate = 10.2 cm³ ÷ 6.5 min = 1.5692... = 1.6 cm³/min (2 s.f.) — Final answer should be rounded to 2 s.f.
>   3 s.f.   2 s.f.

Bar Charts *Can be Used to Show Different Types of Data*

Bar charts can be used to display:

1) <u>Categoric data</u> — data that comes in <u>distinct categories</u>, e.g. flower colour, blood group.
2) <u>Discrete data</u> — data that can be counted in <u>chunks</u>, where there's no in-between value, e.g. number of bacteria is discrete because you can't have half a bacterium.
3) <u>Continuous data</u> — <u>numerical data</u> that can have <u>any value</u> within a <u>range</u>, e.g. length, volume.

There are some <u>golden rules</u> you need to follow for <u>drawing</u> bar charts:

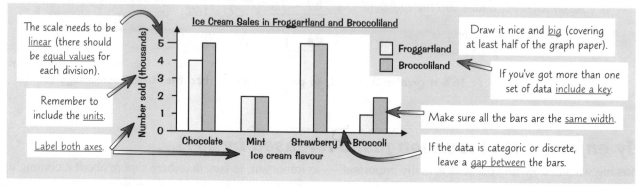

The scale needs to be <u>linear</u> (there should be <u>equal values</u> for each division).

Remember to include the <u>units</u>.

<u>Label both axes</u>.

Ice Cream Sales in Froggartland and Broccoliland

Number sold (thousands)

Chocolate   Mint   Strawberry   Broccoli
Ice cream flavour

Froggartland
Broccoliland

Draw it nice and <u>big</u> (covering at least half of the graph paper).

If you've got more than one set of data <u>include a key</u>.

Make sure all the bars are the <u>same width</u>.

If the data is categoric or discrete, leave a <u>gap between</u> the bars.

Scientific Skills

Processing and Presenting Data

Scatter or Line Graphs Can be Used to Plot Continuous Data

1) If both variables are <u>continuous</u> you can use a <u>scatter graph</u> to show if there is a relationship between them. Here are the <u>rules</u>:

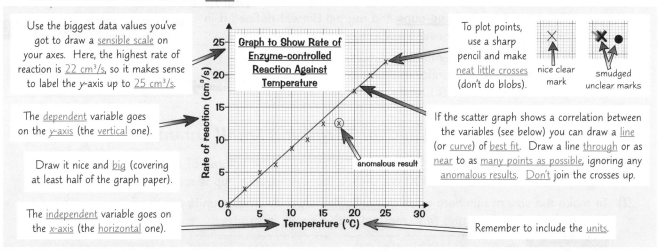

Use the biggest data values you've got to draw a <u>sensible scale</u> on your axes. Here, the highest rate of reaction is <u>22 cm³/s</u>, so it makes sense to label the y-axis up to <u>25 cm³/s</u>.

The <u>dependent</u> variable goes on the <u>y-axis</u> (the <u>vertical</u> one).

Draw it nice and <u>big</u> (covering at least half of the graph paper).

The <u>independent</u> variable goes on the <u>x-axis</u> (the <u>horizontal</u> one).

To plot points, use a sharp pencil and make <u>neat little crosses</u> (don't do blobs). nice clear mark / smudged unclear marks

If the scatter graph shows a correlation between the variables (see below) you can draw a <u>line</u> (or <u>curve</u>) of <u>best fit</u>. Draw a line <u>through</u> or as <u>near</u> to as <u>many points as possible</u>, ignoring any <u>anomalous results</u>. <u>Don't</u> join the crosses up.

Remember to include the <u>units</u>.

2) A <u>line graph</u> is normally used if you're plotting how a <u>variable changes with time</u>. The only difference is that in a line graph, the points are normally <u>joined up</u> by a <u>line</u> or <u>curve</u>.

Graphs Can Give You a Lot of Information About Your Data

1) The <u>gradient</u> (slope) of a graph tells you how quickly the <u>dependent variable</u> changes if you change the <u>independent variable</u>.

$$\text{gradient} = \frac{\text{change in } y}{\text{change in } x}$$

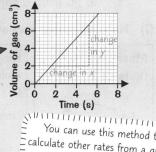

This <u>graph</u> shows the <u>volume of gas</u> produced in a reaction against <u>time</u>. The graph is <u>linear</u> (it's a straight line graph), so you can simply calculate the <u>gradient</u> of the line to find out the <u>rate of reaction</u>.

1) To calculate the gradient, pick <u>two points</u> on the line that are easy to read and a <u>good distance</u> apart.

2) <u>Draw a line down</u> from one of the points and a <u>line across</u> from the other to make a <u>triangle</u>. The line drawn down the side of the triangle is the <u>change in y</u> and the line across the bottom is the <u>change in x</u>.

Change in y = 6.8 − 2.0 = 4.8 cm³   Change in x = 5.2 − 1.6 = 3.6 s

Rate = gradient = $\frac{\text{change in } y}{\text{change in } x} = \frac{4.8 \text{ cm}^3}{3.6 \text{ s}}$ = <u>1.3 cm³/s</u> or <u>1.3 cm³s⁻¹</u>

The units of the gradient are (units of y)/(units of x). cm³/s can also be written as cm³s⁻¹.

You can use this method to calculate other rates from a graph, not just the rate of a reaction. Just remember that a rate is how much something changes over time, so x needs to be the time.

2) The <u>intercept</u> of a graph is where the line of best fit crosses one of the <u>axes</u>. The <u>x-intercept</u> is where the line of best fit crosses the x-axis and the <u>y-intercept</u> is where it crosses the y-axis.

Graphs Show the Relationship Between Two Variables

1) You can get <u>three</u> types of <u>correlation</u> (relationship) between variables:

2) Just because there's correlation, it doesn't mean the change in one variable is <u>causing</u> the change in the other — there might be <u>other factors</u> involved (see page 11).

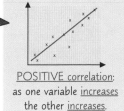
<u>POSITIVE</u> correlation: as one variable <u>increases</u> the other <u>increases</u>.

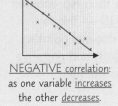
<u>NEGATIVE</u> correlation: as one variable <u>increases</u> the other <u>decreases</u>.

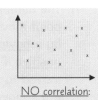
<u>NO</u> correlation: no relationship between the two variables.

I love eating apples — I call it core elation...

Science is all about finding relationships between things. And I don't mean who's going out with who.

Units and Scientific Notation

Graphs and maths skills are all very well, but the numbers don't mean much if you can't get the <u>units</u> right.

S.I. Units Are Used All Round the World

1) It wouldn't be all that useful if I defined volume in terms of <u>bath tubs</u>, you defined it in terms of <u>egg-cups</u> and my pal Sarwat defined it in terms of <u>balloons</u> — we'd never be able to compare our data.

2) To stop this happening, scientists have come up with a set of <u>standard units</u>, called S.I. units, that all scientists use to measure their data. Here are some S.I. units you'll see in biology:

Quantity	S.I. Base Unit
mass	kilogram, kg
length	metre, m
time	second, s

Scaling Prefixes Can Be Used for Large and Small Quantities

1) Quantities come in a huge <u>range</u> of sizes. For example, the volume of a swimming pool might be around 2 000 000 000 cm³, while the volume of a cup is around 250 cm³.

2) To make the size of numbers more <u>manageable</u>, larger or smaller units are used. These are the <u>S.I. base unit</u> (e.g. metres) with a <u>prefix</u> in front:

prefix	tera (T)	giga (G)	mega (M)	kilo (k)	deci (d)	centi (c)	milli (m)	micro (μ)	nano (n)
multiple of unit	10^{12}	10^9	1 000 000 (10^6)	1000	0.1	0.01	0.001	0.000001 (10^{-6})	10^{-9}

3) These <u>prefixes</u> tell you <u>how much bigger</u> or <u>smaller</u> a unit is than the base unit. So one <u>kilometre</u> is <u>one thousand</u> metres.

The conversion factor is the number of times the smaller unit goes into the larger unit.

4) To <u>swap</u> from one unit to another, all you need to know is what number you have to divide or multiply by to get from the original unit to the new unit — this is called the <u>conversion factor</u>.

- To go from a <u>bigger unit</u> (like m) to a <u>smaller unit</u> (like cm), you <u>multiply</u> by the conversion factor.
- To go from a <u>smaller unit</u> (like g) to a <u>bigger unit</u> (like kg), you <u>divide</u> by the conversion factor.

5) Here are some conversions that'll be useful in biology:

Mass can have units of kg and g.	Length can have lots of units, including mm, μm and nm.	Time can have units of min and s.	Volume can have units of m³, dm³ and cm³.
× 1000 kg ⇄ g ÷ 1000	× 1000 × 1000 mm ⇄ μm ⇄ nm ÷ 1000 ÷ 1000	× 60 min ⇄ s ÷ 60	× 1000 × 1000 m³ ⇄ dm³ ⇄ cm³ ÷ 1000 ÷ 1000

You Might Need to Work With Numbers in Scientific Notation

1) Sometimes in biology it's useful to write numbers in <u>scientific notation</u> (sometimes called <u>standard form</u>).

2) This is where you change <u>very big</u> or <u>small</u> numbers with <u>lots of zeros</u> into something more manageable, e.g. 0.017 can be written 1.7×10^{-2}.

3) To do this you just need to <u>move</u> the <u>decimal point</u> left or right.

4) The number of places the decimal point moves is then represented by a <u>power of 10</u> — this is <u>positive</u> if the decimal point's moved to the <u>left</u>, and <u>negative</u> if it's moved to the <u>right</u>.

EXAMPLE: A mitochondrion is approximately 0.0025 mm long. Write this figure in scientific notation.

1) The first number needs to be <u>between 1 and 10</u> so the decimal point needs to move after the '2'.

0.0025

2) <u>Count</u> how many places the decimal point has <u>moved</u> — this is the power of 10. Don't forget the <u>minus</u> sign because the decimal point has moved <u>right</u>.

2.5×10^{-3}

I wasn't sure I liked units, but now I'm converted...

It's easy to get in a muddle when converting between units, but there's a handy way to check you've done it right. If you're moving from a smaller unit to a larger unit (e.g. g to kg) the number should get smaller, and vice versa.

Drawing Conclusions

Congratulations — you're nearly at the end of a gruelling investigation, time to <u>draw conclusions</u>.

You Can Only Conclude What the Data Shows and NO MORE

1) Drawing conclusions might seem pretty straightforward — you just <u>look at your data</u> and <u>say what pattern or relationship you see</u> between the dependent and independent variables.

The table on the right shows the heights of pea plant seedlings grown for three weeks with <u>different fertilisers</u>.

Fertiliser	Mean growth / mm
A	13.5
B	19.5
No fertiliser	5.5

<u>CONCLUSION</u>:
Fertiliser <u>B</u> makes <u>pea plant</u> seedlings grow taller over a <u>three week</u> period than fertiliser A.

2) But you've got to be really careful that your conclusion <u>matches the data</u> you've got and <u>doesn't go any further</u>.

> You <u>can't</u> conclude that fertiliser B makes <u>any other type of plant</u> grow taller than fertiliser A — the results could be totally different.

3) You also need to be able to <u>use your results</u> to <u>justify your conclusion</u> (i.e. back up your conclusion with some specific data).

> Over the three week period, fertiliser B made the pea plants grow <u>6 mm more</u> on average than fertiliser A.

4) When writing a conclusion you need to <u>refer back</u> to the <u>original aim</u>.

> The <u>aim</u> of this experiment might have been to investigate the effect of different fertilisers on the growth of pea plant seedlings. When <u>writing your conclusion</u>, refer back to <u>this aim</u>.

Correlation DOES NOT Mean Cause

If two things are correlated (i.e. there's a relationship between them) it <u>doesn't</u> necessarily mean a change in one variable is <u>causing</u> the change in the other. There are <u>three possible reasons</u> for a correlation:

1) <u>CHANCE</u>: It might seem strange, but two things can show a correlation purely due to <u>chance</u>.

> For example, one study might find a correlation between people's hair colour and how good they are at frisbee. But other scientists <u>don't</u> get a correlation when they investigate it — the results of the first study are just a <u>fluke</u>.

2) <u>LINKED BY A 3RD VARIABLE</u>: A lot of the time it may <u>look</u> as if a change in one variable is causing a change in the other, but it <u>isn't</u> — a <u>third variable links</u> the two things.

> For example, there's a correlation between <u>water temperature</u> and <u>shark attacks</u>. This isn't because warmer water makes sharks crazy. Instead, they're linked by a third variable — the <u>number of people swimming</u> (more people swim when the water's hotter, and with more people in the water you get more shark attacks).

3) <u>CAUSE</u>: Sometimes a change in one variable does <u>cause</u> a change in the other. You can only conclude that a correlation is due to cause when you've <u>controlled all the variables</u> that could, just could, be affecting the result.

> For example, there's a correlation between <u>smoking</u> and <u>lung cancer</u>. This is because chemicals in tobacco smoke cause lung cancer. This conclusion was only made once <u>other variables</u> (such as age and exposure to other things that cause cancer) had been <u>controlled</u> and shown <u>not</u> to affect people's risk of getting lung cancer.

I conclude that this page is a bit dull...

...although, just because I find it dull doesn't mean that I can conclude it's dull (you might think it's the most interesting thing since that kid got his head stuck in the railings near school). In the exam you could be given a conclusion and asked whether some data supports it — so make sure you understand how far conclusions can go.

Uncertainties and Evaluations

Hurrah! The end of another investigation. Well, now you have to work out all the things you did <u>wrong</u>.

Uncertainty is the Amount of Error Your Measurements Might Have

1) <u>Uncertainty</u> is a measure of how <u>confident</u> you are that your results are <u>correct</u>.

2) When you <u>repeat</u> a measurement, you often get a <u>slightly different</u> figure each time you do it due to <u>random error</u> (see page 6). This means that <u>each result</u> has some <u>uncertainty</u> to it.

3) The measurements you make will also have some uncertainty in them due to <u>limits</u> in the <u>resolution</u> of the equipment you use (see page 6).

4) You can <u>reduce</u> the uncertainty by taking <u>repeats</u> and calculating a <u>mean</u>, and by using equipment with a <u>higher resolution</u>.

5) Measuring a <u>greater amount</u> of something also helps to <u>reduce uncertainty</u>. For example, in a rate of reaction experiment, measuring the amount of product formed over a <u>longer period</u> compared to a shorter period will <u>reduce</u> the <u>percentage uncertainty</u> in your results.

Simon had uncertainty about whether this was really his grandma.

Evaluations — Describe How it Could be Improved

An evaluation is a <u>critical analysis</u> of the whole investigation.

1) You should comment on the <u>method</u> — was it <u>valid</u>? Did you control all the other variables to make it a <u>fair test</u>?

2) Comment on the <u>quality</u> of the <u>results</u> — was there <u>enough evidence</u> to reach a valid <u>conclusion</u>? Were the results <u>repeatable</u>, <u>reproducible</u>, <u>accurate</u> and <u>precise</u>?

3) Were there any <u>anomalous</u> results? If there were <u>none</u> then <u>say so</u>. If there were any, try to <u>explain</u> them — were they caused by <u>errors</u> in measurement? Were there any other <u>variables</u> that could have <u>affected</u> the results? You should comment on the level of <u>uncertainty</u> in your results too.

4) All this analysis will allow you to say how <u>confident</u> you are that your conclusion is <u>right</u>.

5) Then you can suggest any <u>changes</u> to the <u>method</u> that would <u>improve</u> the quality of the results, so that you could have <u>more confidence</u> in your conclusion. For example, you might suggest <u>changing</u> the way you controlled a variable, or <u>increasing</u> the number of <u>measurements</u> you took. Taking more measurements at <u>narrower intervals</u> could give you a <u>more accurate result</u>. For example:

> <u>Enzymes</u> have an <u>optimum temperature</u> (a temperature at which they <u>work best</u>). Say you do an experiment to find an enzyme's optimum temperature and take measurements at 10 °C, 20 °C, 30 °C, 40 °C and 50 °C. The results of this experiment tell you the optimum is <u>40 °C</u>. You could then <u>repeat</u> the experiment, taking <u>more measurements around 40 °C</u> to a get a <u>more accurate</u> value for the optimum.

6) You could also make more <u>predictions</u> based on your conclusion, then <u>further experiments</u> could be carried out to test them.

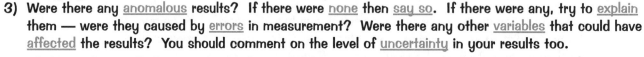

When suggesting improvements to the investigation, always make sure that you say why you think this would make the results better.

Evaluation — next time, I'll make sure I don't burn the lab down...

Well, hopefully you'll have enough scientific skills now to do some awesome investigations. But remember, it's not just in the lab that you'll need your scientific skills knowledge — you can be asked about it in the exam.

Cell Structure

Thankfully there are no prison bars here — you need a <u>microscope</u> to see this type of cell structure...

Animal, Plant and Fungal Cells Have Similarities and Differences

You need to know about a cell's <u>ultrastructure</u> — the parts of a cell you'd see if you viewed it with a <u>very powerful</u> microscope. The different parts of a cell are called <u>subcellular structures</u>. Some subcellular structures have a <u>membrane</u> round them — these can be called <u>organelles</u>. Most <u>animal cells</u> have the following subcellular structures:

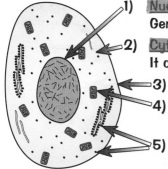

1) <u>Nucleus</u> — contains <u>genetic material</u> that controls the activities of the cell. Genetic material is arranged into <u>chromosomes</u> (see page 22).

2) <u>Cytoplasm</u> — gel-like substance where <u>most of the chemical reactions</u> happen. It contains <u>enzymes</u> (see page 24) that control these chemical reactions.

3) <u>Cell membrane</u> — holds the <u>cell together and controls what goes in and out.</u>

4) <u>Mitochondrion</u> (plural mitochondria) — <u>most of the reactions for respiration</u> take place here (see p.18). <u>Respiration transfers energy</u> that the cell needs to work.

5) <u>Ribosomes</u> — these are involved in <u>protein synthesis</u> (see p.23). They can be found floating in the <u>cytoplasm</u> or attached to the <u>surface</u> of other subcellular structures.

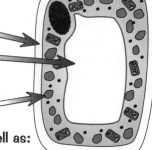

<u>Plant cells</u> usually have <u>all the bits</u> that <u>animal</u> cells have, plus a few <u>extra</u> things that animal cells <u>don't</u> have:

1) <u>Rigid cell wall</u> — made of <u>cellulose</u>. It <u>supports</u> the cell and <u>strengthens it.</u>

2) <u>Large vacuole</u> — contains <u>cell sap,</u> a weak solution of sugar and salts. It maintains the <u>internal pressure</u> to support the cell.

3) <u>Chloroplasts</u> — these are where <u>photosynthesis occurs,</u> which makes food for the plant (see page 52). They contain a <u>green</u> substance called <u>chlorophyll.</u>

<u>Fungal cells</u> usually have all the structures found in <u>animal cells</u> as well as:

1) <u>Cell wall</u> — the <u>structure</u> of a fungal cell wall is <u>different</u> from the structure of a <u>plant cell wall</u> but it has the <u>same function</u> — to <u>support</u> and <u>strengthen</u> the cell.

2) <u>Vacuole(s)</u> — fungal cells can have <u>more than one</u> vacuole and they have many functions in the cell, e.g. maintaining the cell <u>pH</u> and <u>storing</u> small molecules.

Bacterial Cells Have No Nucleus

<u>Bacterial cells</u> are a lot <u>smaller</u> than animal, plant or fungal cells. <u>They lack</u> organelles (e.g. a nucleus, mitochondria, chloroplasts). These are the bits they <u>do</u> have:

1) <u>Chromosomal DNA</u> (<u>one</u> long circular chromosome) — controls the cell's <u>activities</u> and <u>replication</u>. It <u>floats free</u> in the <u>cytoplasm</u> (not in a nucleus).

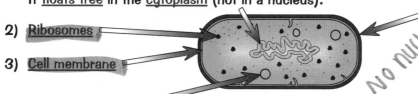

2) <u>Ribosomes</u>

3) <u>Cell membrane</u>

No nucleus

5) <u>Cell wall</u> — the <u>structure</u> is <u>different</u> again from <u>plant</u> and <u>fungal</u> cell walls, but it <u>still</u> does the <u>same</u> thing — providing <u>structural support</u> to the cell.

4) <u>Plasmids</u> — <u>small loops</u> of <u>extra DNA</u> that aren't part of the chromosome. Plasmids contain genes for things like <u>drug resistance</u>, and can be <u>passed</u> between bacteria.

Cell structures — become a property developer...

This page shows 'typical' cells and the subcellular structures they contain. However, cells aren't all the same — they can have different structures depending on the job they do (see page 29 for more).

Q1   Describe the function of these subcellular structures: a) nucleus, b) mitochondria, c) ribosomes. [3 marks]

PRACTICAL   Cells and Microscopes

Ah, the light microscope — that great scientific invention that has enabled us to get up close and personal with the humble cell (and other really small things). Here's how to use one...

You Need to Be Familiar with the Parts of a Light Microscope

Here are the main parts of a light microscope and what they do:

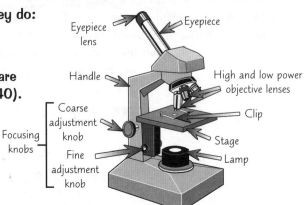

- **Eyepiece lens** — looked through to see the image and also magnifies the image.
- **Objective lens** — magnifies the image. Usually there are three different objective lenses (e.g. ×4, ×10 and ×40).
- **Stage** — supports the slide (see below).
- **Clip** — holds the slide in place.
- **Handle** — to carry the microscope with.
- **Lamp** — shines light through the slide so the image can be seen more easily.
- **Focusing knobs** — move the stage up and down to bring the image into focus.

Specimens Need to be Prepared Before Investigation...

1) Your specimen (the sample you're looking at) needs to let light through it for you to be able to see it clearly — if you've got quite a thick specimen, you'll need to take a thin slice of it to start with.

2) Next, take a clean slide (a strip of clear glass or plastic) and use a pipette to put one drop of water or mountant (a clear, gloopy liquid) in the middle of it — this will secure the specimen in place.

3) Use tweezers to place your specimen on the slide.

4) Add a drop of stain if needed — if your specimen is completely transparent or colourless, a drop of stain is added to make the specimen easier to see. Different stains are used to highlight different structures or tissues. For example, eosin is used to stain cytoplasm and methylene blue stains DNA.

5) Place a cover slip (a square of thin, transparent plastic or glass) at one end of the specimen, holding it at an angle with a mounted needle.

6) Carefully lower the cover slip onto the slide. Press it down gently with the needle so that no air bubbles are trapped under it.

... Then You're Ready for Viewing

1) Start by clipping the slide containing your specimen onto the stage.

2) Select the lowest-powered objective lens (i.e. the one that produces the lowest magnification).

3) Use the coarse adjustment knob to move the stage up to just below the objective lens. Then, looking down the eyepiece, move the stage downwards (so you don't accidently crash the slide into the lens) until the specimen is just about in focus.

4) Then, still looking down the eyepiece, adjust the focus with the fine adjustment knob, until you get a clear image of your specimen.

5) If you need to see your specimen with greater magnification, swap to a higher-powered objective lens and refocus.

> A higher magnification isn't always a good thing — if your specimen is relatively big you might not be able to see the whole thing. It can also be difficult to focus at high magnifications.

Objective lenses — glasses for people with a biased view...

There's some important stuff about using microscopes here — they can be really useful, so get learning.

Q1   A scientist wants to use a light microscope to view the cell walls of a colourless sample of plant tissue.
Describe how she could prepare a slide containing the tissue, where the cell walls are visible.   [4 marks]

Calculating Cell Size

PRACTICAL

Microscopes let you see small things like cells, but if you want to know just how small they really are then you'll need to know how to measure them. You might even need to play around with a formula — how fun.

You Can Measure the Size of a Single Cell

When viewing cells under a microscope, you might need to work out their size. You could work out the size of a single cell like this:

1) Place a clear, plastic ruler on top of your microscope slide. Clip the ruler and slide onto the stage.

2) Select the objective lens that gives an overall magnification of x 100.

3) Adjust the focus to get a clear image of the cells.

4) Move the ruler so that the cells are lined up along 1 mm. Then count the number of cells along this 1 mm sample.

5) 1 mm = 1000 μm. So to calculate the length of a single cell in μm, you just need to divide 1000 μm by the number of cells in the sample. E.g. if you counted 4 cells in 1 mm, the length of a single cell would be: 1000 ÷ 4 = 250 μm.

You could also calculate the breadth (width) of the cells by turning the ruler 90 degrees and then measuring again.

6) Alternatively, you might be told the diameter of the field of view. Then all you have to do is estimate how many cells fit across the diameter and divide the diameter by this number.

field of view
(view down the microscope)

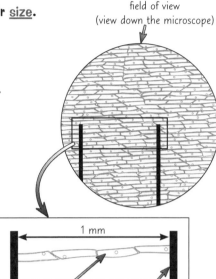

1 mm

cell   ruler marking

You Can Use a Formula to Calculate Cell Size

This handy formula is used to calculate the magnification of an image: ⟶

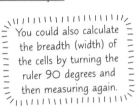

$$\text{magnification} = \frac{\text{image size}}{\text{real size}}$$

Image size and real size should have the same units. If they don't, you'll need to convert them first (see page 10).

But you can also use the formula to calculate the size of the cells you're looking at. You need to rearrange the formula — this formula triangle might help:

They were much bigger in the picture.

Cover up the thing you're trying to find. The parts you can still see are the formula you need to use.

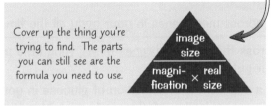

image size

magni- × real
fication   size

EXAMPLE: The image of a specimen is 2 mm wide when viewed under a magnification of x 100. Calculate the width of the specimen. Give your answer in μm.

1) Rearrange the formula.   real size = image size ÷ magnification
2) Fill in the values you know.   real size = 2 ÷ 100
3) Remember the units in your answer.   = 0.02 mm
4) Convert the units.   = 20 μm

Remember, to convert from millimetres (mm) to micrometres (μm), you need to multiply by 1000 (see p.10). E.g. 0.02 mm × 1000 = 20 μm.

Single cells — they're just focussing on their career right now...

You could get asked a question about calculating cell size in your exam. Take the time now to get the hang of it and then if it comes up on exam day you can bag yourself some easy marks.

Q1 The diagram shows onion cells viewed under a microscope. Calculate the approximate length of a single cell. Give your answer in μm.   [2 marks]

0.6 mm

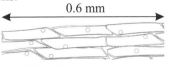

high concentration ——> low concentration

Diffusion

Substances need to move <u>in</u> and <u>out</u> of cells. <u>One</u> of the <u>ways</u> that this can happen is by <u>diffusion</u>.

Cell Membranes Contain Phospholipids and Proteins

1) In order to function normally, cells need to <u>take in</u> and <u>get rid</u> of many different <u>substances</u>.

2) To get in or out of a cell, substances need to <u>pass across</u> the <u>cell membrane</u>. All cell membranes have the same basic <u>structure</u>.

3) A cell membrane is <u>selectively permeable</u> — this means it lets <u>some</u> substances pass across but <u>not others</u>.

4) <u>Small</u>, <u>uncharged</u> substances (e.g. oxygen, carbon dioxide) can pass <u>directly</u> through the <u>phospholipids</u>.

5) Some <u>larger</u> or <u>charged</u> substances (e.g. glucose, ions) can still pass through the membrane, but they can only get across through the <u>protein channels</u>.

6) Some <u>very large</u> substances (e.g. starch) <u>can't</u> pass through the membrane at all.

7) There are <u>differences</u> between the <u>concentration</u> of substances <u>inside a cell</u> and <u>in its environment</u> (the fluid or air that surrounds it) — this can also affect <u>how</u> substances <u>get in and out</u> of the cell.

proteins — these form 'channels' in the membrane

Outside cell

phospholipid molecules arranged in a double layer

Inside cell (cytoplasm)

A phospholipid is a type of lipid with a phosphate group attached.

Diffusion is the Movement of Particles from Higher to Lower Concentration

1) Many substances pass in or out of a cell through the process of <u>diffusion</u>.

2) <u>Diffusion</u> is simple. It's just the <u>gradual movement</u> of particles from where there are <u>lots</u> of them to where there are <u>fewer</u> of them. That's all it is — just the <u>natural tendency</u> for stuff to <u>spread out</u>. Here's the fancy definition:

> Diffusion is the <u>net (overall) movement</u> of <u>particles</u> from an area of <u>higher concentration</u> to an area of <u>lower concentration</u>.

Particles include molecules and ions.

3) If something <u>moves</u> from an area of <u>higher concentration</u> to an area of <u>lower concentration</u> it is said to have moved <u>down</u> its <u>concentration gradient</u>.

4) Diffusion is an example of <u>passive transport</u> — any process in which particles move across a cell membrane by travelling <u>down</u> their concentration gradient <u>without</u> needing <u>energy</u>.

Osmosis is also a form of passive transport (see next page).

Diffusion is Really Important

Substances are <u>diffusing</u> across membranes in your <u>body</u> all the time. Here are a couple of examples:

1) <u>Glucose</u> diffuses across the <u>cell membranes</u> of <u>villi</u> (tiny little projections on the inside of your <u>gut</u>).

2) When you've eaten a meal, the concentration of glucose in your <u>gut</u> is <u>likely</u> to be <u>higher</u> than the concentration of glucose in your <u>blood</u>. So glucose <u>diffuses</u> across the cell membranes of your gut <u>into</u> your blood.

3) Molecules move about <u>randomly</u> of course, so glucose molecules actually go <u>both</u> ways across the membrane — but if there are a lot <u>more</u> molecules on the gut side of the membrane, there's a <u>net</u> (overall) movement <u>from</u> that side.

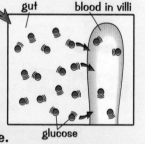

gut   blood in villi

glucose

1) <u>Carbon dioxide</u> and <u>oxygen</u> diffuse across cell membranes in your lungs. The <u>lungs</u> contain millions and millions of little air sacs called <u>alveoli</u> where <u>gas exchange</u> happens (see p.46).

2) The <u>blood</u> passing next to the alveoli has just returned to the lungs from the rest of the body, so it contains <u>lots</u> of <u>carbon dioxide</u> and <u>very little oxygen</u>. When you've just breathed in, <u>oxygen</u> diffuses <u>out</u> of the <u>alveoli</u> (high concentration) into the <u>blood</u> (low concentration). <u>Carbon dioxide</u> diffuses <u>out</u> of the <u>blood</u> (high concentration) into the <u>alveoli</u> (low concentration) to be breathed out.

Sadly, this information won't just diffuse into your head...

...so you're going to have to learn it the old fashioned way. Go back and make sure you've learnt any new terms.

Q1   Explain why diffusion is classed as a method of 'passive transport'.   [2 marks]

Osmosis and Active Transport

If you loved the previous page then you're in luck — here are <u>two</u> more ways stuff <u>gets across cell membranes</u>.

Osmosis is a Special Case of Diffusion, That's All

> <u>Osmosis</u> is the <u>net movement of water molecules</u> through a <u>selectively permeable membrane</u> from a region of <u>higher water concentration</u> to a region of <u>lower water concentration</u>.

1) <u>Water molecules</u> are small enough to pass through <u>selectively permeable membranes</u> (see previous page).

2) The water molecules actually pass <u>both ways</u> through the membrane during <u>osmosis</u>. This happens because water molecules <u>move about randomly</u> all the time.

3) But because there are <u>more</u> water molecules on one side than on the other, there's a steady <u>net flow</u> of water into the region with <u>fewer</u> water molecules, e.g. into the <u>sucrose</u> solution.

4) This means the <u>sucrose</u> solution gets more <u>dilute</u>. The water acts like it's trying to <u>even up</u> the concentration either side of the membrane.

5) Osmosis <u>doesn't require energy</u>, so it's a method of <u>passive transport</u> (see previous page).

cell membrane

sucrose too large to pass through membrane

water   sucrose solution

Net movement of water molecules

Osmosis Can Affect the Structure of Cells

Turgid cell

Plasmolysed cell

1) If the <u>water concentration</u> in a solution surrounding a <u>plant cell</u> is <u>higher</u> than inside the cell, water will be <u>drawn into</u> the cell by <u>osmosis</u> until it becomes <u>turgid</u> (plump and swollen). The contents of the cell <u>push</u> against the cell wall.

2) However, if a <u>plant cell</u> is in a solution with a <u>very low</u> water concentration, water will <u>move out</u> of the cell. The <u>cytoplasm</u> inside the cell will start to <u>shrink</u> and the <u>membrane</u> will <u>pull away</u> from the <u>cell wall</u>. A cell in this condition is said to be <u>plasmolysed</u>.

3) <u>Animal cells</u> don't have <u>cell walls</u> to help protect them, so they're <u>more affected</u> by their <u>surroundings</u>. Animal cells will <u>lose water</u> and <u>shrink</u> if they're surrounded by a solution with a <u>lower water concentration</u> than them. They can even take in <u>too much</u> water and <u>burst</u> if they're surrounded by a solution with a <u>higher water concentration</u> than them.

4) If a <u>plant or animal cell</u> is in a solution which has the <u>same</u> water concentration as the cell itself, then the structure of the cell <u>won't</u> be affected because there's <u>no</u> net movement of water in <u>either direction</u>.

Active Transport is Not a Passive Process

moving up the concentration gradient

<u>Active transport</u> is another process used to <u>move</u> substances <u>in and out</u> of cells. It's kind of the <u>opposite</u> of <u>diffusion</u>. Here's the <u>definition</u>:

> <u>Active transport</u> is the <u>movement of particles</u> across a membrane <u>against</u> a concentration gradient (i.e. from an area of <u>lower</u> to an area of <u>higher concentration</u>) <u>using energy</u> transferred during respiration.

During active transport, molecules and ions are moved <u>up a concentration gradient</u> by the <u>proteins</u> in the cell membrane.

See the next page for more on respiration.

Try saying osmosis backwards — it's not that fun, or educational...

Osmosis is why it's bad to drink sea water. The high salt content means you end up with a much lower water concentration in your blood than in your cells. Lots of water moves out of your cells making them shrivel and die.

Q1   Give the definition of active transport.   [2 marks]

Q2   A piece of carrot is placed in a solution of lower water concentration than its cells. Suggest what will happen to the cells in the carrot. Explain your answer.   [2 marks]

Respiration

You need energy to keep your body going. Energy comes from food, and it's transferred by respiration.

Respiration is NOT "Breathing In and Out"

1) Respiration is the process of releasing the chemical energy that's stored in glucose (a sugar).

2) Plants make their own glucose for respiration through photosynthesis (see p.52). Animals produce glucose by breaking down carbohydrates in the food they eat.

3) Organisms need the energy transferred by respiration to survive — so respiration happens continuously in every cell in all living organisms.

4) The break down of glucose is used to make a substance called ATP, which stores the energy in cells. When a cell needs energy, ATP molecules are broken down and energy is released. The energy is used for essential processes, such as cell division, protein synthesis, active transport (see p.17), contracting muscles (in animals only) and the transmission of nerve impulses (also in animals only).

5) Cellular respiration actually involves several different chemical reactions, which are all controlled by enzymes, so the overall rate of respiration is affected by temperature and pH.

See page 24 for more on enzymes.

6) There are two types of respiration, aerobic respiration and fermentation.

① glucose
pyruvate
↓
2 atp

② pyruvate
( )
carbon dioxide water
lots ATP

oxygen

Aerobic Respiration Needs Plenty of Oxygen

1) Aerobic respiration is what happens when there's plenty of oxygen available.

2) First, a glucose molecule is broken down into two molecules of pyruvate. This releases enough energy to produce two molecules of ATP.

3) Then, if oxygen is available, the two pyruvate molecules are broken down and the products are combined with oxygen to make carbon dioxide (CO_2) and water. This releases enough energy to make lots of ATP.

More ATP is made through aerobic respiration than is made through fermentation — see next page.

4) Here is the overall word summary for aerobic respiration:

glucose + oxygen ⟶ carbon dioxide + water + energy

5) The first step of respiration, the break down of glucose to pyruvate, happens in the cell cytoplasm.

6) The rest of the aerobic respiration process takes place in mitochondria (see p.13). The mitochondria contain most of the enzymes needed to control aerobic respiration reactions.

Bacteria don't have mitochondria, so all of their aerobic respiration reactions take place in the cytoplasm.

7) Cells with a higher energy requirement have more mitochondria to meet their energy needs. For example, muscle cells use lots of energy for muscle contraction, so they contain lots of mitochondria.

Aerobic — mmm, a biscuit covered in light, bubbly chocolate...

Thank goodness for respiration — transferring the energy stored in my tea and biscuits to my brain cells. Great.

Q1   During aerobic respiration, where within the cell is glucose broken down into pyruvate?   [1 mark]

Q2   Give two essential cell processes which use energy stored in ATP.   [2 marks]

Q3   Give the word summary for aerobic respiration.   [2 marks]

More on Respiration

Now for the second type of respiration — fermentation. It's actually more interesting than aerobic respiration.

Fermentation Doesn't Use Oxygen At All

1) Fermentation takes place when there's little or no oxygen present.

2) Just like in aerobic respiration (see previous page), the process starts off when a glucose molecule is broken down into two pyruvate molecules. As in aerobic respiration, this process happens in the cytoplasm and releases enough energy to produce two molecules of ATP.

3) But then, because there's not enough oxygen present, respiration takes a fermentation pathway.

4) The pathway always takes place in the cytoplasm, but it's slightly different in different organisms. In animals, pyruvate molecules are converted to lactate, but in plants and yeast, pyruvate is converted to ethanol and carbon dioxide.

Yeast are organisms made from just one (fungal) cell.

5) Here are the word summaries you need to learn for fermentation:

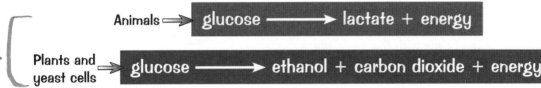

Animals ⟹ glucose ⟶ lactate + energy

Plants and yeast cells ⟹ glucose ⟶ ethanol + carbon dioxide + energy

Here's a Handy Table Comparing Aerobic Respiration and Fermentation

	Aerobic Respiration	Fermentation
Conditions	Oxygen present	Not enough oxygen present
Reactants	Glucose and oxygen	Glucose
Products	Carbon dioxide and water	In animals — lactate In plants and yeast cells — ethanol and carbon dioxide
ATP yield	High — lots of ATP made per molecule of glucose	Much lower — only 2 ATP made per molecule of glucose

The substances used in chemical reactions are the reactants and the substances made are the products.

You Can Do Experiments to Investigate the Rate of Respiration

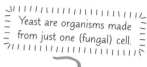

PRACTICAL

Here's a nice little experiment that you can do to measure the rate of fermentation in yeast:

1) Put a set volume and concentration of glucose in a test tube.

2) Put the test tube in a water bath set to 25 °C.

3) Add a set mass of yeast to the test tube and stir for 2 minutes.

4) Add a layer of oil to stop oxygen reaching the yeast.

5) Attach the test tube to a gas syringe (as shown in the diagram) and measure the volume of CO_2 produced in a set amount of time (e.g. 10 minutes).

bung
gas syringe
test tube
oil
water bath
yeast and glucose

6) If you divide the volume of CO_2 produced by the time taken to produce it, you can calculate the average rate of respiration.

7) You could then repeat the experiment but change one of the variables (like temperature or pH) and compare your results to investigate the effect of that factor on the respiration rate.

Respiration transfers energy — but this page has worn me out...

Make sure you learn those word summaries and know the differences between aerobic respiration and fermentation.

Q1 What is pyruvate converted to during fermentation in plants? [1 mark]

PRACTICAL Investigating Respiration

I'm afraid you're not done with respiration yet — here's another way that you can investigate it. This time it involves a fancy piece of apparatus called a respirometer. Time to get hands on with some little critters.

Respirometers are Used to Measure Rate of Respiration in Small Organisms

In aerobic respiration, organisms use up oxygen from the air. By measuring the amount of oxygen consumed by organisms in a given time, you can calculate their rate of respiration. Here's an experiment which uses woodlice, a water bath and a respirometer. It allows you to measure the effect of temperature on the rate of respiration of the woodlice. (You could use germinating peas or beans instead of woodlice. Germinating seeds respire to provide energy for growth.)

1) Firstly, some soda lime granules are added to two test tubes. Soda lime absorbs the CO_2 produced by the respiring woodlice in the experiment.

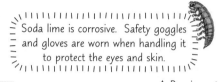
Soda lime is corrosive. Safety goggles and gloves are worn when handling it to protect the eyes and skin.

2) A ball of cotton wool is placed above the soda lime in each tube. Woodlice are placed on top of the cotton wool in one tube. Glass beads with the same mass as the woodlice are used in the control tube. (There's more on controls on page 5.)

3) The respirometer is then set up as shown in the diagram.

Make sure the woodlice don't come into contact with the soda lime.

4) The syringe is used to set the fluid in the manometer to a known level.

5) The apparatus is then left for a set period of time in a water bath set to 15 °C.

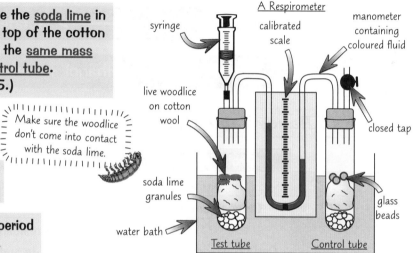
A Respirometer
syringe · calibrated scale · manometer containing coloured fluid · closed tap · live woodlice on cotton wool · soda lime granules · water bath · glass beads · Test tube · Control tube

6) During this time, there'll be a decrease in the volume of the air in the test tube containing the woodlice. This is because the woodlice use up oxygen in the tube as they respire. (The CO_2 they produce is absorbed by the soda lime so it doesn't affect the experiment.)

7) The decrease in volume reduces the pressure in the tube, causing the coloured liquid in the manometer to move towards the test tube containing the woodlice.

You can also use cotton wool soaked in a few drops of potassium hydroxide solution to absorb the CO_2.

8) The distance moved by the liquid in a given time is measured. This value can then be used to calculate the volume of oxygen taken in by the woodlice per minute. This gives you the average rate of respiration in, e.g. cm^3/min.

9) Repeat steps 1-8 with the water bath set at different temperatures, e.g. 20 °C and 25 °C. This will allow you to see how changing the temperature affects the rate of respiration.

Any live animals you use in this experiment should be treated ethically. E.g. it's important not to leave the woodlice in the respirometer for too long, or they may run out of oxygen and die. There's more on the ethical treatment of organisms in experiments on page 74.

My rate of respiration has increased after all that...

Controls are mega important in experiments — they check that the thing you're observing (e.g. respiring woodlice) is what's affecting the results and nothing else. So you should make sure everything else is kept exactly the same.

Q1 A student is carrying out an experiment to measure the effect of temperature on the rate of respiration in germinating beans.
  a) What could the student use as her control? [1 mark]
  b) What could she use to keep the beans at different temperatures? [1 mark]

Revision Questions for Section 1a

Well, that wraps up Section 1a — now it's time for some questions to see if you've been paying attention...

- Try these questions and tick off each one when you get it right.
- When you've done all the questions for a topic and are completely happy with it, tick off the topic.

Cells and Microscopes (p.13-15) ☐

1) What is the function of a cell membrane? Controls which enters + exists cell
2) Describe the function of cell walls. Supports cell
3) True or False? Fungal cells have a vacuole. true
4) In what type of cell are plasmids found? bacterial
5) On a light microscope, what is the function of the lamp?
6) Why is it important to take a thin slice of your specimen when preparing a microscope slide?
7) Why might you use a stain when preparing a microscope slide?
8) A tissue sample is viewed under a microscope using a magnification of × 100.
   Describe how you could measure the size of a single cell using a clear plastic ruler.

Diffusion, Osmosis and Active Transport (p.16-17) ☐

9) Describe the basic structure of a cell membrane.
10) Explain why a cell membrane is described as being selectively permeable.
11) Give one function of a protein channel in a cell membrane.
12) Define diffusion.
13) True or False? Passive transport requires energy.
14) Give one example of a situation where diffusion occurs in the body.
15) Define osmosis.
16) Explain how a plant cell becomes turgid.
17) What happens to the structure of a plant cell when it becomes plasmolysed?
18) What can happen to an animal cell if it's surrounded by a solution with a high water concentration?
19) Give two ways in which active transport differs from diffusion.

Respiration (p.18-20) ☐

20) What is respiration?
21) Which type of respiration requires oxygen?
22) Where in a cell do the final stages of aerobic respiration take place?
23) Why do some cells have lots of mitochondria?
24) How many ATP molecules are produced in fermentation?
25) What are the products of fermentation in animals?
26) What could you measure to calculate the rate of aerobic respiration in animals?

DNA and Genes

DNA is a big, big deal in biology, but the mystery of its structure was only solved relatively recently. Luckily, you get to learn all about it, so pen at the ready, thinking cap on... woah there, we nearly forgot the biscuits...

Chromosomes Are Really Long Molecules of DNA

1) DNA stands for deoxyribonucleic acid. It's the chemical that all of the genetic material in a cell is made up from.

2) It contains coded information — basically all the instructions to put an organism together and make it work.

3) So it's what's in your DNA that determines what inherited characteristics you have.

4) DNA is found in the nucleus of animal and plant cells, in really long structures called chromosomes.

5) Chromosomes normally come in pairs.

6) A gene is a small section of DNA found on a chromosome.

7) Each gene codes for (tells the cells to make) a specific protein (there's loads more about this on the next page).

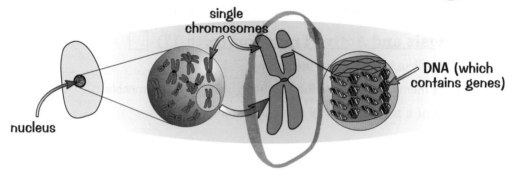

single chromosomes

DNA (which contains genes)

nucleus

You Need to Know About the Structure of DNA

1) DNA is a double helix (a double-stranded spiral). Each of the two DNA strands is made up of lots of nucleotides joined together in a long chain.

2) Each nucleotide contains a small molecule called a "base". The order of these bases makes up the genetic code.

3) DNA has just four different bases.

4) The bases are A (adenine), C (cytosine), G (guanine) and T (thymine).

5) Each base forms cross links to a base on the other strand. This keeps the two DNA strands tightly wound together.

6) A always pairs up with T, and C always pairs up with G. This is called complementary base-pairing.

complementary base pairs

A — T

C — G

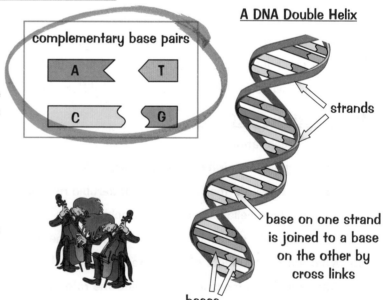

A DNA Double Helix

strands

base on one strand is joined to a base on the other by cross links

bases

Complementary base pairs — oh A, darling, you are stunning...

The complementary base-pairing thing is mega important in protein synthesis (see next page) so make sure you've got your head around it. Then you can treat yourself to some twisty crisps and imagine you're eating DNA.

Q1   Which base always pairs with adenine in a molecule of DNA?   [1 mark]

Q2   What is a gene?   [2 marks]

Protein Synthesis

So here's how <u>life</u> works — <u>DNA molecules</u> contain a <u>genetic code</u> that determines which <u>proteins</u> are built. The proteins determine how all the <u>cells</u> in the body <u>function</u>. Simple, eh.

Proteins are Made by Reading the Code in DNA

1) As you saw on the previous page, DNA tells the cells which proteins to make.

2) <u>Proteins</u> are made up of chains of molecules called <u>amino acids</u>. Each different protein has its own particular <u>number</u> and <u>order</u> of amino acids.

3) It's the <u>order</u> of the <u>bases</u> in a <u>gene</u> that decides the <u>order</u> of <u>amino acids</u> in a protein.

4) Each gene contains a <u>different sequence</u> of bases — which is what allows it to code for a <u>particular protein</u>.

Proteins are Synthesised on Ribosomes in the Cytoplasm

<u>DNA</u> is found in the cell <u>nucleus</u> and can't move out of it because it's <u>really big</u>. The cell needs to get the information from the DNA to <u>ribosomes</u> in the cell <u>cytoplasm</u> where proteins are synthesised. This is done using a molecule called <u>messenger RNA</u> (<u>mRNA</u>), which is <u>similar</u> to DNA, but it's <u>shorter</u> and only a <u>single strand</u>. Here's how it's done:

1) The <u>DNA</u> contains the <u>gene</u> coding for the <u>protein</u>.

2) In the nucleus, the two DNA strands <u>unzip</u> around the gene. The DNA is used as a <u>template</u> to make the <u>mRNA</u>. <u>Base pairing</u> ensures it's <u>complementary</u> (it matches the opposite strand).

3) The <u>mRNA</u> molecule then moves <u>out of the nucleus</u> and into the <u>cytoplasm</u>, where it attaches to a <u>ribosome</u>.

4) <u>Amino acids</u> that match the <u>code</u> on the mRNA are <u>joined together</u> in the correct order. This makes the <u>protein</u> coded for by the gene.

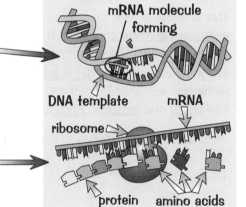

Proteins Have Many Different Functions

When a chain of amino acids has been assembled, it <u>folds</u> into a <u>unique shape</u> which allows the protein to <u>perform</u> the task it's meant to do. Here are a few examples of types of protein:

1) ENZYMES — act as <u>biological catalysts</u> to <u>speed up</u> chemical reactions in the body (see p.24).

2) HORMONES — used to <u>carry messages</u> around the body. E.g. <u>insulin</u> is a hormone released into the blood by the pancreas to <u>regulate</u> the <u>blood sugar level</u> (see p.39-40).

3) STRUCTURAL PROTEINS — are physically <u>strong</u>. E.g. <u>collagen</u> is a structural protein that strengthens <u>connective tissues</u> (like ligaments and cartilage).

4) ANTIBODIES — produced by <u>white blood cells</u> to help the body <u>fight disease</u> (see p.45).

5) RECEPTORS — found in <u>cell membranes</u>. When a molecule (e.g. a hormone) <u>binds</u> to a receptor it triggers a <u>change</u> inside the cell.

People aged over 12 and under 20 are just great — I'm pro-teen...

Protein synthesis isn't the easiest of topics. Remember, the order of bases in the DNA is copied into mRNA, which then moves to the ribosomes. Here, the chain of amino acids is assembled according to the order of the bases.

Q1 Describe the role of mRNA in the production of proteins. [2 marks]

Enzymes

Enzymes are the magicians of the protein world — they speed up reactions without being changed themselves.

Enzymes Are Catalysts Produced by Living Things

1) Living things have thousands of different chemical reactions going on inside them all the time. These reactions need to be carefully controlled — to get the right amounts of substances.

2) You can usually make a reaction happen more quickly by raising the temperature. This would speed up the useful reactions but also the unwanted ones too... not good. There's also a limit to how far you can raise the temperature inside a living creature before its cells start getting damaged.

3) So... all living cells produce enzymes that act as biological catalysts. A catalyst is a substance which increases the speed of a reaction, without being changed or used up in the reaction.

4) Enzymes reduce the need for high temperatures and we only have enzymes to speed up the useful chemical reactions in the body.

Enzymes Have Special Shapes So They Can Catalyse Reactions

1) Enzyme activity converts substrates (molecules that enzymes act on) into one or more products.

2) Every enzyme has an active site — the part where it joins onto its substrates to catalyse the reaction.

3) Enzymes are really picky — they usually only catalyse one specific reaction.

4) This is because, for the enzyme to work, the substrates have to fit into the active site and form an enzyme-substrate complex. If the shape of the substrates isn't complementary to the enzyme's active site, then the reaction won't be catalysed.

5) Enzymes can catalyse degradation reactions (when molecules are split apart) or synthesis reactions (when molecules are joined together). E.g. the enzyme catalase catalyses the break down of hydrogen peroxide into water and oxygen. Phosphorylase catalyses the synthesis of starch from glucose-1-phosphate.

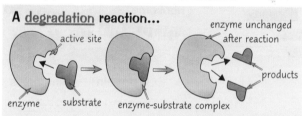

A degradation reaction...

enzyme unchanged after reaction

active site

products

enzyme   substrate   enzyme-substrate complex

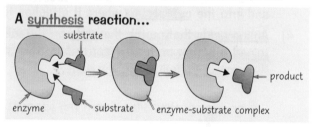

A synthesis reaction...

substrate

product

enzyme   substrate   enzyme-substrate complex

Enzymes Need the Right Temperature and pH

A protein is held together with bonds. Temperature and pH can disrupt these bonds, which can change the shape of the protein. For enzymes, this could alter the rate at which it catalyses a reaction:

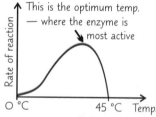

This is the optimum temp. — where the enzyme is most active

Rate of reaction

O °C   45 °C   Temp.

1) Temperature — like with any reaction, a higher temperature increases the rate at first. But if it gets too hot, some of the bonds holding the enzyme together break. This changes the shape of the enzyme's active site, so the substrate won't fit any more. The enzyme is said to be denatured. All enzymes have an optimum temperature that they work best at.

2) pH — if pH is too high or too low, it interferes with the bonds holding the enzyme together. This changes the shape of the active site and denatures the enzyme. All enzymes have an optimum pH that they work best at. It's often neutral pH 7, but not always.

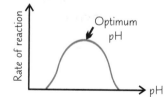

Rate of reaction

Optimum pH

pH

If only enzymes could speed up revision...

Make sure you use the special terms like 'active site' and 'denatured' — the examiners will love it.

Q1   Explain why enzymes have an optimum pH.

[2 marks]

Investigating Enzyme Activity

You'll soon know how to investigate the effect of a variable on the rate of enzyme activity... I bet you're thrilled.

You Can Investigate How Temperature Affects Enzyme Activity | PRACTICAL

You Can Measure How Fast a Product Appears...

1) The enzyme catalase catalyses the breakdown of hydrogen peroxide into water and oxygen.

2) You can collect the oxygen and measure how much is produced in a set time.

3) Use a pipette to add a set amount of hydrogen peroxide to a boiling tube. Put the tube in a water bath at 10 °C.

4) Set up the rest of the apparatus as shown. Add a source of catalase (e.g. 1 cm³ of potato) to the hydrogen peroxide and quickly attach the bung.

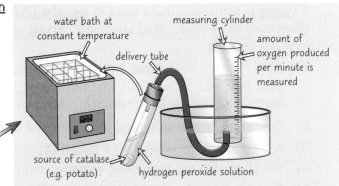

5) Record how much oxygen is produced in the first minute. Repeat three times and calculate the mean.

6) Repeat at 20 °C, 30 °C and 40 °C.

7) Control any variables (e.g. pH, the potato used, the size of potato pieces, etc.) to make it a fair test.

...Or How Fast a Substrate Disappears

1) The enzyme amylase catalyses the breakdown of starch to maltose.

2) It's easy to detect starch using iodine solution — if starch is present, the iodine solution will change from browny-orange to blue-black.

3) Set up the apparatus as in the diagram. Put a drop of iodine solution into each well on the spotting tile. Every ten seconds, drop a sample of the mixture into a well using a pipette. When the iodine solution remains browny-orange (i.e. starch is no longer present) record the total time taken.

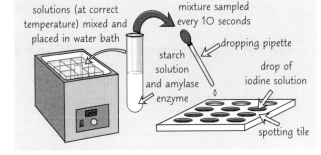

4) Repeat with the water bath at different temperatures to see how it affects the time taken for the starch to be broken down. Remember to control all of the variables each time.

You Can Also Investigate How pH Affects Enzyme Activity | PRACTICAL

1) You can adapt these experiments to investigate the effect of pH on enzyme activity.

2) Follow the same method, but add a buffer solution with a different pH level to a series of different tubes containing the enzyme-substrate mixture.

3) As before, control any variables — use the water bath to keep the temperature of the reaction mixture the same for each pH, and make sure volumes and concentrations are kept the same.

Mad scientists — they're experi-mental...

The key thing with experiments is to only change the thing you're testing — and absolutely nothing else. Sorted.

Q1   An experiment is carried out to investigate the effect of temperature on the breakdown of hydrogen peroxide by the enzyme catalase. Cubes of potato are used as a source of catalase. Suggest two variables that would need to be controlled in this experiment.   [2 marks]

Section 1b — DNA and Proteins

Genetic Engineering

Genetic engineering involves modifying an organism's DNA to introduce desirable characteristics. Our old friends, enzymes, play an important role in the process.

Genetic Engineering Transfers Genes Between Organisms

The basic idea of genetic engineering is to transfer a gene responsible for a desirable characteristic from one organism to another, so that the organism that receives the gene also has the desirable characteristic. A vector is something that's used to transfer DNA into a cell. Plasmids (see p.13) are often used as vectors. They are small, circular molecules of DNA that can be transferred between bacteria.

Viruses can also be used as vectors.

You need to learn these steps involved in genetic engineering:

1) Scientists take an organism that has a useful characteristic and identify the section of DNA that carries the gene for the useful characteristic on one of the organism's chromosomes.

2) The useful gene is extracted (cut) from the organism's chromosome using enzymes.

3) A plasmid is then taken from a bacterium.

4) The plasmid is cut open using enzymes and the useful gene is inserted into it, again using enzymes.

5) The plasmid is then inserted into a host bacterium. The host bacterium is now a genetically modified (GM) organism — it should display the characteristic that the useful gene codes for.

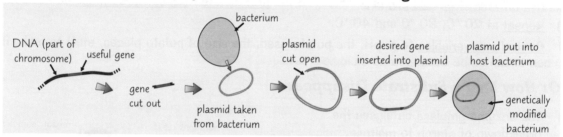

DNA (part of chromosome) useful gene — gene cut out — plasmid taken from bacterium — bacterium — plasmid cut open — desired gene inserted into plasmid — plasmid put into host bacterium — genetically modified bacterium

Genetic Engineering Has Many Different Uses

1) It's not always bacteria that have their genes modified — genetic engineering can also be used to modify other organisms (this can be done by 'infecting' an organism with a vector containing the desired gene).

2) GM organisms can be very useful, especially in agriculture and medicine. For example:

- The gene for human insulin has been inserted into bacteria. The bacteria are grown in large numbers to produce insulin for the treatment of diabetes (see p.40).

- A gene that helps fish to survive in cold water has been inserted into tomato plants to help the plants survive at low temperatures.

- A gene that leads to the production of beta-carotene has been inserted into rice plants. The 'golden rice' produced by these plants can be eaten by people in developing countries to help protect them from a serious nutrient deficiency.

- A gene for a poison that kills insect pests can be taken from a bacterium and inserted into crop plants. This makes the plants resistant to the insect pests (see p.66).

3) Genetic engineering is quite a controversial topic — not everyone thinks it's a good idea.

4) There are worries about the long-term effects of genetic engineering — that changing an organism's genes might accidentally create unplanned problems, which could get passed on to future generations.

I say it's great.

5) Some people think that eating GM crops could adversely affect human health.

Coming soon, plants that'll whine if they've not got enough water...

Genetically modified organisms could potentially be very useful, but some people are worried about using them. Make sure you know the steps involved in genetic engineering and when enzymes are used in the process.

Q1 Describe the role of bacterial plasmids in genetic engineering.

[1 mark]

Revision Questions for Section 1b

Well, that's Section 1b done with — just a page of revision questions to go, then you can put your feet up.
* Try these questions and tick off each one when you get it right.
* When you've done all the questions for a topic and are completely happy with it, tick off the topic.

DNA and Genes (p.22) ☑

1) Describe the role of DNA.
2) Describe the basic structure of DNA.
3) What are the four different bases found in a DNA molecule?
4) Describe what is meant by 'complementary base-pairing'.

Protein Synthesis (p.23) ☐

5) Name the smaller molecules that proteins are made from.
6) Why is the base sequence in a gene important in protein synthesis?
7) Explain how genetic information is carried from the nucleus of a cell to the cytoplasm.
8) Name the structure in a cell on which proteins are made.
9) Name five different types of proteins.

Enzymes (p.24-25) ☑

10) Why can enzymes be described as biological catalysts?
11) What is an enzyme's 'active site'?
12) Why do enzymes only usually catalyse one specific reaction?
13) What happens to a substrate molecule during a degradation reaction?
14) What does it mean when an enzyme has been 'denatured'?
15) Give two things that you could measure to determine the rate of an enzyme-controlled reaction.

Genetic Engineering (p.26) ☐

16) Describe the basic meaning of 'genetic engineering'.
17) In genetic engineering, scientists first identify a gene for a useful characteristic in an organism. Describe the next step in the process.
18) Why does a bacterial plasmid need to be cut open in genetic engineering?
19) Describe two reasons why enzymes are used during genetic engineering.
20) What is a 'genetically modified' organism?

Mitosis

In order to survive and grow, our <u>cells</u> have got to be able to <u>divide</u>. And that means our DNA as well...

Chromosomes Contain Genetic Information

1) Most cells in your body have a <u>nucleus</u>. The nucleus contains your <u>genetic material</u> in the form of <u>chromosomes</u>. Chromosomes are <u>coiled up</u> lengths of <u>DNA molecules</u> (see p.22 for more on DNA).

2) <u>Body cells</u> normally have <u>two copies</u> of each <u>chromosome</u> — this makes them '<u>diploid</u>' cells. One chromosome comes from the organism's '<u>mother</u>', and one comes from its '<u>father</u>'.

3) The total number of <u>chromosomes</u>, counting <u>both copies</u>, is called the <u>diploid chromosome complement</u>.

4) When a cell divides by <u>mitosis</u> (see below) it makes two cells <u>identical</u> to the original cell — the nucleus of each new cell contains the <u>same number of chromosomes</u> as the original cell.

Mitosis Makes New Cells for Growth and Repair

1) <u>Body cells</u> in <u>multicellular</u> organisms <u>divide</u> to produce new cells during a process called the <u>cell cycle</u>. The stage of the cell cycle when the cell divides is called <u>mitosis</u>.

2) Multicellular organisms use <u>mitosis</u> to <u>grow</u> or to <u>replace cells</u> that have been <u>damaged</u>.

3) You need to know what happens before and during <u>mitosis</u>:

The
Cell
Cycle

Mitosis

In a cell that's not dividing, the DNA is all spread out in <u>long strings</u>. Before mitosis occurs, the cell has to <u>grow</u> and to <u>increase</u> the amount of <u>subcellular structures</u> such as <u>mitochondria</u> and <u>ribosomes</u>. It then <u>duplicates</u> its <u>DNA</u> — so there's one copy for each new cell. The DNA is copied and forms <u>X-shaped</u> chromosomes. Each 'arm' of the chromosome is called a <u>chromatid</u> and is an <u>exact duplicate</u> of the other.

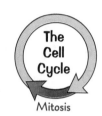

The left arm has the same DNA as the right arm of the chromosome.

Once its contents and DNA have been copied, the cell is ready for <u>mitosis</u>. Mitosis is divided into <u>four stages</u>:

1) The chromosomes <u>condense</u>, getting shorter and fatter. The <u>membrane</u> around the <u>nucleus breaks down</u> and the chromosomes <u>lie free</u> in the cytoplasm.

2) The chromosomes <u>line up</u> along the <u>equator</u> (centre) of the cell.

3) Fibres in the cell called <u>spindle fibres</u> pull the chromosomes apart. The <u>two chromatids</u> for each chromosome go to <u>opposite ends</u> of the cell.

4) <u>Membranes</u> form around each of the sets of chromosomes. These become the <u>nuclei</u> of the two new cells — the <u>nucleus</u> has <u>divided</u>.

Before the last stage ends, the <u>cytoplasm</u> and <u>cell membrane</u> divide to form two separate cells.

4) At the end of mitosis, the cell has produced <u>two new daughter cells</u>. Each daughter cell contains exactly the <u>same sets of chromosomes</u> in its nucleus as the other daughter cell — they're <u>genetically identical diploid cells</u>. They're also genetically identical to the <u>parent cell</u>.

5) This means that the <u>diploid chromosome complement</u> stays the <u>same</u> and no <u>genetic information</u> is lost.

6) You can <u>calculate</u> the <u>number of cells</u> there'll be after <u>multiple divisions</u> of a cell by mitosis. The formula you need is: <u>number of cells = 2^n</u>, where '<u>n</u>' is the <u>number of divisions</u> by mitosis.

E.g. if you start with 1 cell, after <u>5</u> divisions of mitosis there'll be 2^5 = 2 × 2 × 2 × 2 × 2 = <u>32 cells</u>.

A cell's favourite computer game — divide and conquer...

Mitosis can seem tricky at first. But don't worry — just go through it slowly, one step at a time.

Q1   Give two uses for mitosis in multicellular organisms.   [2 marks]

Cell Specialisation and Stem Cells

Multicellular organisms have lots of cells. All of the cells start off exactly the same but then some biological wizardry causes them to change depending on their function. It's clever stuff.

Most Cells are Specialised for a Specific Job

1) Specialisation is the process by which a cell changes to become adapted for its particular function.

2) In most animal cells, the ability to specialise is lost at an early stage, but lots of plant cells don't ever lose this ability.

3) Having specialised cells is important — it allows organisms to work more efficiently.

4) Most cells are specialised to carry out a particular job. For example:

PALISADE LEAF CELLS

- Palisade leaf cells do most of the photosynthesis in plants, so they are packed with chloroplasts (see p.13).

- Their tall shape means they have a lot of surface area exposed down the side for absorbing CO_2 from the air in the leaf, and their thin shape means that you can fit loads of them in at the top of a leaf, so they're nearer the light.

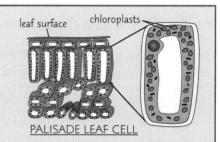

leaf surface   chloroplasts

PALISADE LEAF CELL

NEURONS (NERVE CELLS)

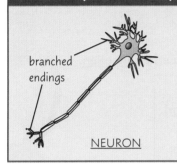

branched endings

NEURON

- The function of neurons is to carry electrical signals from one part of the body to another.

- These cells are long (to cover more distance) and have branched connections at their ends to connect to other nerve cells and form a network throughout the body.

There's more about neurons on page 37.

Stem Cells can Become Different Types of Specialised Cells

1) Stem cells are unspecialised. Depending on what instructions they're given, stems cells can self-renew, where they divide by mitosis to become new stem cells, or they can develop into new types of cell.

2) Embryonic stem cells are found in very early embryos. They have the potential to turn into any kind of cell at all. This makes sense if you think about it — all the different types of cell found in an animal have to come from those few cells in the embryo.

3) This means stem cells are really important for the growth and development of organisms.

4) It's not just embryos that contain stem cells — they're found throughout life. But once an organism's developed, stem cells are only found in certain tissues, like bone marrow. These tissue stem cells aren't as versatile as embryonic stem cells — they can't turn into any cell type at all, only certain ones from the tissue they originally came from.

5) Tissue stem cells are used to replace damaged cells, e.g. to make new skin or blood cells.

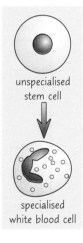

unspecialised stem cell

specialised white blood cell

Tissue stem cells are also called 'adult stem cells'.

That year everyone forgot my birthday, I felt like a stem cell...

...not special at all. It still hurts. But enough of that, let's see if you're specialised to answer this question...

Q1   Give one way in which tissue stem cells differ from embryonic stem cells.   [1 mark]

Cell Organisation

Some organisms contain loads of <u>cells</u>, but how, you might wonder, do all these cells end up making a working human or squirrel... the answer's <u>organisation</u>. Without it, they'd just make a meaty splodge.

Cells in Multicellular Organisms are Arranged in a Hierarchy

1) <u>Cells</u> are the <u>basic building blocks</u> that make up <u>all living organisms</u>.
2) As you know from the previous page, cells aren't all the same — most are <u>specialised</u> to carry out a <u>particular function</u>.
3) <u>Multicellular organisms</u> contain a large <u>variety</u> of different types of <u>specialised cells</u>.
4) The cells form part of a <u>hierarchy</u> that makes up the entire organism. The hierarchy goes like this: <u>specialised cells</u> → <u>tissues</u> → <u>organs</u> → <u>systems</u>.

Similar Cells are Organised into Tissues

A <u>tissue</u> is a <u>group</u> of <u>similar cells</u> that work together to carry out a particular <u>function</u>. It can include <u>more than one type</u> of specialised cell.

Epithelial cell

less than 0.1 mm

In <u>mammals</u> (like humans), examples of tissues include:
1) <u>Muscular tissue</u>, which <u>contracts</u> (shortens) to <u>move</u> whatever it's attached to.
2) <u>Glandular tissue</u>, which <u>makes</u> and <u>secretes</u> chemicals like <u>enzymes</u> and <u>hormones</u>.
3) <u>Epithelial tissue</u>, which <u>covers</u> some parts of the body, e.g. the <u>inside</u> of the <u>gut</u>.

Epithelial tissue

Tissues are Organised into Organs

An <u>organ</u> is a group of <u>different tissues</u> that work together to perform a certain <u>function</u>.

For example, the <u>stomach</u> is an organ made of these tissues:
1) <u>Muscular tissue</u>, which moves the stomach wall to <u>churn up the food</u>.
2) <u>Glandular tissue</u>, which makes <u>digestive juices</u> to digest food.
3) <u>Epithelial tissue</u>, which covers the <u>outside</u> and <u>inside</u> of the stomach.

Stomach

Organs are Organised into Systems

A <u>system</u> is a <u>group of organs</u> working together to perform a particular <u>function</u>.

about 10 cm (over 1000 times longer than an epithelial cell)

Salivary glands

For example, the <u>digestive system</u> (found in humans and other mammals) <u>breaks down</u> and <u>absorbs</u> food. It's made up of these organs:
1) <u>Glands</u> (e.g. the <u>pancreas</u> and <u>salivary glands</u>), which produce <u>digestive juices</u>.
2) The <u>stomach</u> and <u>small intestine</u>, which <u>digest</u> food.
3) The <u>liver</u>, which produces <u>bile</u>.
4) The <u>small intestine</u>, which <u>absorbs</u> soluble <u>food</u> molecules.
5) The <u>large intestine</u>, which <u>absorbs water</u> from undigested food, leaving <u>faeces</u>.

Liver

Digestive system

Stomach

Pancreas

Small intestine

Large intestine

<u>Systems</u> work together to make entire <u>organisms</u>.

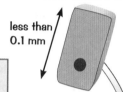

Soft and quilted — the best kind of tissues...

So in summary, an organism consists of systems, which are groups of organs, which are made of tissues, which are groups of cells working together. Now just for the thrill of it, here's a practice question.

Q1 The bladder is an organ. Explain what this means. [2 marks]

Sexual Reproduction

Sexual reproduction is really important to organisms — without it there would be no babies to coo over...

Sexual Reproduction Produces Genetically Different Cells

1) Sexual reproduction is where genetic information from two organisms (a 'father' and a 'mother') is combined to produce offspring which are genetically different to either parent.

2) In sexual reproduction, the parents produce gametes (reproductive cells).

3) Gametes only contain half the number of chromosomes of body cells — they are haploid. Body cells (with the full number of chromosomes) are diploid (see p.28).

4) Gametes from the male parent are called sperm and gametes from the female parent are called eggs.

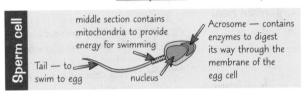

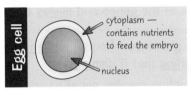

These diagrams aren't drawn to scale — egg cells are actually much bigger than sperm cells.

Fertilisation is the Fusion of Gametes

1) At fertilisation, a male gamete combines with a female gamete to produce a fertilised egg, also known as a zygote. The two haploid nuclei of the gametes fuse together so the zygote ends up with the full set of chromosomes (so it is diploid).

gametes   zygote

2) The zygote then undergoes cell division (by mitosis — see p.28) and develops into an embryo.

3) The embryo inherits characteristics from both parents, as it has received a mixture of chromosomes (and therefore genes) from its mum and its dad.

You Need to Know Where Gametes are Made in Animals and Plants

In animals, sperm cells are produced in the testes and egg cells are produced in the ovaries. This is where they're located in humans:

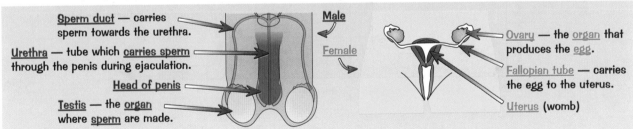

Sperm duct — carries sperm towards the urethra.

Urethra — tube which carries sperm through the penis during ejaculation.

Head of penis

Testis — the organ where sperm are made.

Male

Female

Ovary — the organ that produces the egg.

Fallopian tube — carries the egg to the uterus.

Uterus (womb)

In plants, sperm cells are produced in the stamen and egg cells are produced in the carpel. These organs are both found in the flower:

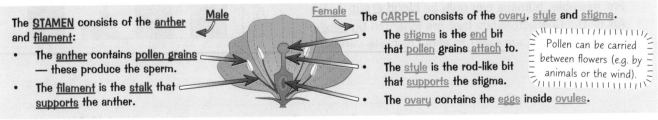

The STAMEN consists of the anther and filament:
- The anther contains pollen grains — these produce the sperm.
- The filament is the stalk that supports the anther.

Male

Female

The CARPEL consists of the ovary, style and stigma.
- The stigma is the end bit that pollen grains attach to.
- The style is the rod-like bit that supports the stigma.
- The ovary contains the eggs inside ovules.

Pollen can be carried between flowers (e.g. by animals or the wind).

No joke on this page I'm afraid — ahhh I'm just pollen your leg...

So, in sexual reproduction two haploid nuclei (one from a male gamete, one from a female gamete) fuse together.

Q1   The haploid gamete of a plant species has 12 chromosomes. The nucleus of two of these gametes fuse to make a zygote. How many chromosomes will there be in the zygote?   [1 mark]

Variation

Variety is the spice of life they say. Well then, this page is well spicy — it's all about variety within species.

Organisms of the Same Species Have Differences

1) Different species look... well... different — my dog definitely doesn't look like a daisy.

2) But even organisms of the same species will usually look at least slightly different — e.g. in a room full of people you'll see different colour hair, individually shaped noses, a variety of heights, etc.

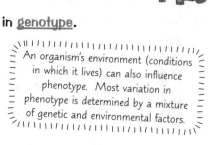

3) These differences are called the variation within a species.

4) Variation can be genetic — this means it's caused by differences in genotype. Genotype is all of the genes and alleles that an organism has.
(Alleles are just versions of genes — there's more about them on the next page.)
An organism's genotype affects its phenotype — the characteristics that it displays.

An organism's environment (conditions in which it lives) can also influence phenotype. Most variation in phenotype is determined by a mixture of genetic and environmental factors.

5) Sexual reproduction creates genetic variation as each offspring ends up with a different combination of its parents' genes.

6) Different genes control different characteristics. Some characteristics are controlled by a single gene (e.g. having wet or dry earwax) so the characteristic is inherited by single gene inheritance. However, most characteristics are controlled by several genes interacting (e.g. skin colour) so they are inherited by polygenic inheritance.

Variation can be Continuous or Discrete

Continuous variation is when the individuals in a population vary within a range — there are no distinct categories, e.g. humans can be any height within a range, not just tall or short. Other examples include an organism's mass, and the number of leaves on a tree. Characteristics that are inherited by polygenic inheritance usually show continuous variation.

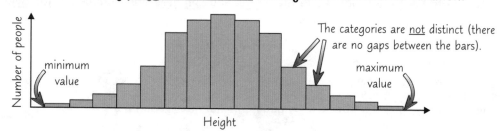

The categories are not distinct (there are no gaps between the bars).

Discrete variation is when there are two or more distinct categories — each individual falls into only one of these categories, there are no intermediates. For example, humans can only be blood group A, B, AB or O. Characteristics that are inherited by single gene inheritance are likely to show discrete variation.

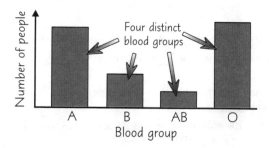

Four distinct blood groups

Your meanotype determines how nice you are to your sibling...

Make sure you properly understand all of the new terms you've come across on this page. If you forget what they mean you can always come back to refresh you memory. That's the good thing about books, the pages will always be there. They can't run away, barking into the sunset, like my favourite pet daisy did...

Q1 Cystic fibrosis is a disease caused by a single gene. Is the presence of cystic fibrosis in a population likely to be an example of continuous or discrete variation? Explain your answer. [2 marks]

Genetic Diagrams

It's time to get a bit mystic now — this page is about predicting how different characteristics will be inherited.

Alleles Are Different Versions of the Same Gene

1) All genes exist in different versions called alleles (which are represented by letters in genetic diagrams).

2) You have two versions (alleles) of every gene in your body — one on each chromosome in a pair.

3) If an organism has two alleles for a particular gene that are the same, then it's homozygous for that trait. If its two alleles for a particular gene are different, then it's heterozygous.

4) Some alleles are dominant (shown with a capital letter, e.g. 'C') and some are recessive (shown by a small letter, e.g. 'c'). Dominant alleles overrule recessive alleles, so if an organism has one dominant and one recessive allele for a gene (e.g. 'Cc'), then the dominant allele will determine what characteristic is present.

5) To display a dominant characteristic, an organism can have either two dominant alleles for a particular gene or one dominant and one recessive allele for that gene. But for an organism to display a recessive characteristic, both its alleles must be recessive.

6) Remember an organism's genotype is the combination of genes and alleles it has, and its phenotype is the characteristics that it displays.

Genetic Diagrams Can Show the Inheritance of a Single Characteristic

The inheritance of a single characteristic is called monohybrid inheritance. You can use a monohybrid cross to show how recessive and dominant traits for a single characteristic are inherited.

For example, let's say an allele that causes hamsters to have superpowers is recessive ('b'), and that normal (boring) hamsters don't have superpowers due to a dominant allele ('B'). Here's how you could use a monohybrid cross to show the probability of either the dominant or recessive trait being inherited:

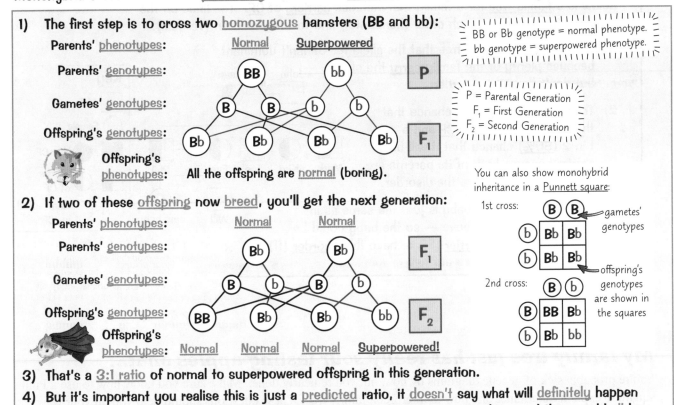

3) That's a 3:1 ratio of normal to superpowered offspring in this generation.

4) But it's important you realise this is just a predicted ratio, it doesn't say what will definitely happen — e.g. it's possible that four hamsters could be born in the F_2 generation here and they could all be superpowered. This is mainly because which gametes combine during fertilisation is completely random.

Genetic diagrams can be allele bit confusing...

Remember, genetic diagrams only tell you probabilities. They don't say what will definitely happen.

Q1   An organism displays a recessive characteristic. What does this tell you about its genotype?   [1 mark]

More on Genetic Diagrams

Here's another page of funny diagrams with squares, circles and lines making pretty patterns. Enjoy...

Family Trees Can Also Show Monohybrid Inheritance

Knowing how inheritance works helps you to interpret a family tree.
Here's a worked example using cystic fibrosis (CF) — a genetic disorder of the cell membranes.

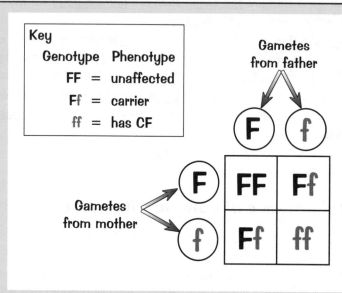

Key

Genotype	Phenotype
FF =	unaffected
Ff =	carrier
ff =	has CF

Gametes from father

Gametes from mother

	F	f
F	FF	Ff
f	Ff	ff

1) The allele which causes CF is a recessive allele, 'f', carried by about 1 person in 30.

2) Because it's recessive, people with only one copy of the allele won't have the disorder — they're known as carriers.

3) For a child to have a chance of inheriting the disorder, both parents must either have the disorder themselves or be carriers.

4) As the Punnett square shows, there's a 1 in 4 (25%) chance of a child having the disorder if both parents are carriers.

5) The probability of each outcome can also be expressed as a ratio — 1 : 2 : 1 for unaffected : carrier : disorder.

Below is a family tree for a family that includes carriers of CF. The lines on the tree link the parents to each other (horizontal) and to their children (vertical).

1) You can see from the tree that the allele for CF isn't dominant because plenty of the family carry the allele but don't have the disorder.

2) There is a 1 in 4 (25%) chance that the new baby will have CF and a 1 in 2 (50%) chance that it will be a carrier because both of its parents are carriers but don't have the disorder.

3) The case of the new baby is just the same as in the Punnett square above — so the baby could be unaffected (FF), a carrier (Ff) or have the disorder (ff).

John   Susan

Mark   Kim   Joe   Eve   Phil

Will   new baby   ?

Key

Male
Female
Has CF
Carrier of CF
Unaffected by CF

Remember, the probabilities are only predictions. Eve and Phil could have, for example, eight children who are all unaffected by CF.

My family tree just has really sour tasting apples on it...

You're probably sick of genetic diagrams by now, but you're nearly done. Make sure you know how to use a Punnett square to explain inheritance and how to interpret a family tree. These questions should help you on your way...

Q1 Use the family tree above for the following questions.

a) Mark and his wife (who is not shown in the diagram) have a baby with cystic fibrosis. What are the possible genotypes of Mark's wife? [1 mark]

b) Draw a Punnett square to show the predicted phenotype ratio for the offspring of John and Susan. Give your ratio as unaffected : carrier : disorder. [3 marks]

c) Explain why the predicted ratio in your answer to part b) is different from the actual ratio of phenotypes of John and Susan's offspring as shown in the family tree. [1 mark]

Revision Questions for Section 2a

Well, that wraps up Section 2a — let's see how much information you've managed to store in that noggin.
- Try these questions and tick off each one when you get it right.
- When you've done all the questions for a topic and are completely happy with it, tick off the topic.

Mitosis, Cell Specialisation and Cell Organisation (p.28-30) ☐

1) What does it mean if a cell is diploid?
2) True or False? Mitosis produces two genetically identical cells.
3) What is a chromatid?
4) Describe what happens in the four main stages of mitosis.
5) Give one example of a specialised cell found in the human body.
6) What are stem cells?
7) How do stem cells self-renew?
8) What is a tissue?
9) Which word completes this sentence? A group of organs working together is called a _____.

Sexual Reproduction (p.31) ☐

10) What is a haploid cell?
11) Draw a labelled diagram of a sperm cell.
12) What is fertilisation?
13) Are zygotes haploid or diploid?
14) In animals, where are egg cells produced?
15) Name the male and female reproductive organs found within a flower.

Variation and Genetic Diagrams (p.32-34) ☐

16) What is variation?
17) Describe what is meant by an organism's: a) genotype, b) phenotype.
18) Give one way in which genetic variation in a species can be caused.
19) What is polygenic inheritance?
20) What is continuous variation?
21) Are characteristics that show continuous variation usually inherited by single gene or polygenic inheritance?
22) What is an allele?
23) Explain what it means to be homozygous for a trait.
24) What does it mean if an allele is dominant?
25) What does F_1 stand for on a genetic diagram?
26) Where on a Punnett square would you write the offspring's genotypes?
27) In family trees, what does it mean if two people are joined directly by a horizontal line?

The Nervous System

Right, it's time to get your <u>brain cells</u> fired up — this section's a <u>corker</u>. First up, the <u>nervous system</u>.

The Brain and Spinal Cord make up the Central Nervous System (CNS)

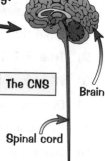

1) The nervous system is made up of <u>neurons</u> (nerve cells) which go to <u>all parts</u> of the body.

2) The <u>central nervous system</u> (CNS) consists of the <u>brain</u> and <u>spinal cord</u> only.

3) The <u>spinal cord</u> is a long column of <u>neurons</u> that run from the <u>base of the brain</u> down the <u>spine</u>. At several places down the cord, neurons <u>branch off</u> and <u>connect</u> with other parts of the body. The spinal cord <u>relays information</u> between the <u>brain</u> and the <u>rest of the body</u>.

4) The brain is made up of <u>billions</u> of <u>interconnected neurons</u>.

5) The brain is in charge of all of our <u>complex behaviours</u>. It controls and coordinates everything you do — running, breathing, sleeping, remembering your gym kit...

6) <u>Different regions</u> of the brain carry out <u>different functions</u>. For example:

The CNS | Brain

Spinal cord

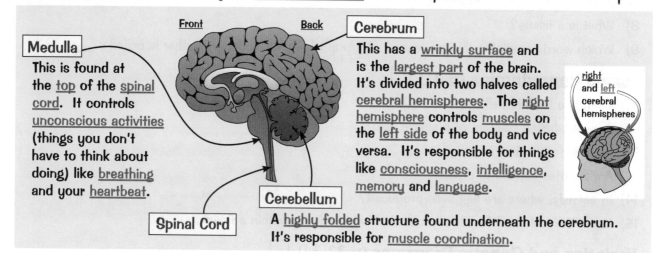

Medulla

This is found at the <u>top</u> of the <u>spinal cord</u>. It controls <u>unconscious activities</u> (things you don't have to think about doing) like <u>breathing</u> and your <u>heartbeat</u>.

Front   Back

Spinal Cord

Cerebellum

A <u>highly folded</u> structure found underneath the cerebrum. It's responsible for <u>muscle coordination</u>.

Cerebrum

This has a <u>wrinkly surface</u> and is the <u>largest part</u> of the brain. It's divided into two halves called <u>cerebral hemispheres</u>. The <u>right</u> hemisphere controls <u>muscles</u> on the <u>left side</u> of the body and vice versa. It's responsible for things like <u>consciousness</u>, <u>intelligence</u>, <u>memory</u> and <u>language</u>.

right and <u>left</u> cerebral hemispheres

The CNS Coordinates a Response

1) The body has lots of sensory <u>receptors</u> — groups of <u>cells</u> that can detect a <u>change in your environment</u> (a <u>sensory input</u> or <u>stimulus</u>). Thinking about your <u>senses</u> gives you an idea of the sensory receptors you have. For example, in order to <u>see</u>, receptors in your <u>eyes</u> detect <u>light</u>, in order to <u>hear</u>, receptors in your <u>ears</u> detect <u>sound waves</u>, etc.

2) When a <u>stimulus</u> is detected by <u>receptors</u>, the information is <u>converted</u> to a <u>nervous (electrical) impulse</u> and sent along <u>sensory neurons</u> to the <u>CNS</u>.

There's more about the different types of neuron on the next page.

3) The CNS <u>coordinates</u> the response (in other words, it <u>decides what to do</u> about the stimulus and tells something to do it). Impulses travel <u>through the CNS</u> along <u>interneurons</u>.

4) The CNS sends information to an <u>effector</u> (<u>muscle</u> or <u>gland</u>) along a <u>motor neuron</u>. The effector then <u>responds</u> accordingly — e.g. a <u>muscle</u> may <u>contract</u> or a <u>gland</u> may <u>secrete a hormone</u> (see page 39).

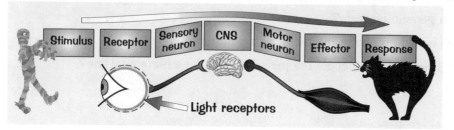

Stimulus | Receptor | Sensory neuron | CNS | Motor neuron | Effector | Response

Light receptors

The time it takes you to respond to a stimulus is called your reaction time.

That big squidgy thing in your head is pretty impressive really...

Make sure you know how the different parts of the nervous system work together to coordinate a response.

Q1   Describe the function of the cerebellum.

[1 mark]

Neurons and Synapses

You might be wondering what happens when an impulse reaches the end of a neuron. Or you might not. Either way, I'll tell you. But before that, a bit on the three different types of neuron...

Neurons Transmit Information Rapidly as Electrical Impulses

1) All neurons have a cell body with a nucleus (plus cytoplasm and other subcellular structures).

2) The cell body has extensions that connect to other neurons — dendrites and dendrons carry nerve impulses towards the cell body, and axons carry nerve impulses away from the cell body.

3) Some axons are surrounded by a myelin sheath. This acts as an electrical insulator, speeding up the electrical impulse.

4) Neurons can be very long, which also speeds up the impulse (connecting with another neuron slows the impulse down, so one long neuron is much quicker than lots of short ones joined together).

5) You need to know about sensory, motor and inter neurons:

SENSORY NEURON
- One long dendron carries nerve impulses from receptor cells to the cell body, which is located in the middle of the neuron.
- One short axon carries nerve impulses from the cell body to the CNS.

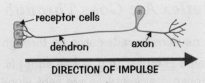

MOTOR NEURON
- Many short dendrites carry nerve impulses from the CNS to the cell body.
- One long axon carries nerve impulses from the cell body to effector cells.

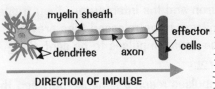

The diagram shows a myelinated motor neuron but you can get unmyelinated ones too. Sensory neurons and interneurons can also be myelinated.

INTERNEURON
- Many short dendrites carry nerve impulses from sensory neurons to the cell body.
- An axon carries nerve impulses from the cell body to motor neurons.

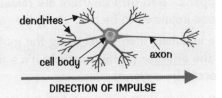

Synapses Connect Neurons

1) The connection between two neurons is called a synapse.

2) The nerve signal is transferred by chemicals called neurotransmitters, which diffuse (move) across the gap.

3) The neurotransmitters then set off a new electrical signal in the next neuron.

4) The transmission of a nervous impulse is very fast, but it is slowed down a bit at the synapse because the diffusion of neurotransmitters across the gap takes time.

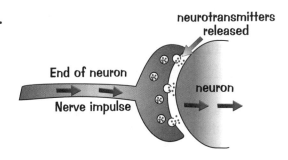

Don't let the thought of exams play on your nerves...

There's a bit more on neurons and synapses on the next page. Make sure that you've got the different types of neuron, and how impulses are passed between them at synapses, clear in your head before you move on.

Q1   Where do sensory neurons carry information from?   [1 mark]

Q2   Which type of neuron carries information from the CNS to effector cells?   [1 mark]

Q3   Describe how a nerve signal is transferred between two neurons.   [2 marks]

38

Reflexes

Your brain can decide how to respond to a stimulus pretty quickly. But sometimes waiting for your brain to make a decision is just too slow. That's why you have reflexes.

Reflexes Help Prevent Injury

1) Reflexes are automatic responses to certain stimuli — they can reduce the chances of being injured.

- If you touch a hot object, you automatically move your hand away from it — you don't have to decide to do it.
- If someone shines a bright light in your eyes, your pupils automatically get smaller so that less light gets into the eyes — this stops them getting damaged (see below).

2) The route taken by the information in a reflex (from receptor to effector) is called a reflex arc.

The Reflex Arc Goes Through the Central Nervous System

1) The neurons in reflex arcs go through the spinal cord or through an unconscious part of the brain.

2) When a stimulus (e.g. a bee sting) is detected by receptors, impulses are sent along a sensory neuron to an interneuron in the CNS.

3) When the impulses reach a synapse between the sensory neuron and the interneuron, they trigger neurotransmitters to be released (see previous page). These cause impulses to be sent along the interneuron.

4) When the impulses reach a synapse between the interneuron and a motor neuron, the same thing happens. Neurotransmitters are released and cause impulses to be sent along the motor neuron.

5) The impulses then travel along the motor neuron to the effector (in this example it's a muscle, but it could be a gland).

6) The muscle then contracts and moves your hand away from the bee.

7) Because you don't have to spend time thinking about the response, it's quicker than normal responses.

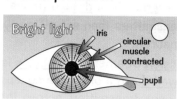

5. Impulses travel along a motor neuron, via a synapse.

4. Impulses are passed along an interneuron, via a synapse.

6. When impulses reach muscle, it contracts.

3. Impulses travel along the sensory neuron.

2. Stimulation of the pain receptor.

spinal cord (remember, in some reflexes the impulse would go through an unconscious part of the brain instead)

1. Cheeky bee stings finger.

A Reflex Helps to Protect the Eye

1) Very bright light can damage the eye — so you have a reflex to protect it.

2) Light receptors in the eye detect very bright light and send a message along a sensory neuron to the brain.

3) The message then travels along an interneuron to a motor neuron, which tells circular muscles in the iris (the coloured part of the eye) to contract, making the pupil smaller.

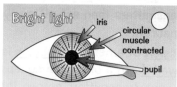

Bright light — iris, circular muscle contracted, pupil

Reflex — but only if she hasn't noticed how muscly you are already...

Reflexes bypass conscious parts of your brain completely when a super quick response is essential — your body just gets on with things. If you had to stop and think first, you'd end up a lot more sore (or worse).

Q1   A chef touches a hot tray. A reflex reaction causes him to immediately move his hand away.
  a) Give the effector in this reflex arc.   [1 mark]
  b) Suggest where in the CNS the interneurons involved in this reflex arc are located.   [1 mark]

Section 2b — Control and Communication

The Endocrine System

The other way to send information around the body (apart from along neurons) is by using hormones.

Hormones Are Chemical Messengers Sent in the Blood

1) Hormones are chemical messengers released directly into the blood. They are carried in the blood to other parts of the body.

2) They travel all over the body but they only affect particular cells in particular places.

3) The affected cells are called target cells. A tissue that contains target cells is called a target tissue.

4) Target cells contain receptor proteins that are complementary to specific hormones. This means that only cells that have the receptors will respond to the hormone.

5) When hormones bind to receptors it triggers a change inside the cell.

6) Hormones control things in organs and cells that need constant adjustment. They tend to have relatively long-lasting effects.

7) Hormones are produced in (and released by) various glands, called endocrine glands. These glands make up your endocrine system.

8) Here are some examples of endocrine glands and the hormones they release:

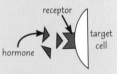

Being complementary means that the hormone and the receptor have shapes that fit together.

THE PANCREAS

This produces the hormones insulin and glucagon, which regulate the blood glucose level (see next page).

TESTES — males only

Produce testosterone — a hormone which controls puberty and sperm production in males.

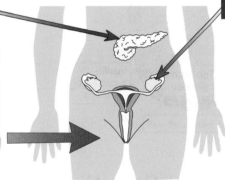

OVARIES — females only

Release hormones involved in the menstrual cycle, e.g. oestrogen.

The menstrual cycle is the monthly sequence of events in which the female body releases an egg and prepares the uterus (womb) in case it receives a fertilised egg.

Hormonal and Nervous Responses Have Differences

NERVOUS RESPONSE:
Very FAST action.
Acts for a very SHORT TIME.
Acts on a very PRECISE AREA.

HORMONAL RESPONSE:
SLOWER action.
Acts for a LONG TIME.
Acts in a more GENERAL way.

So if you're not sure whether a response is nervous or hormonal, have a think...

1) If the response is really quick, it's probably nervous. Some information needs to be passed to effectors really quickly (e.g. pain signals, or information from your eyes telling you about the lion heading your way), so it's no good using hormones to carry the message — they're too slow.

2) But if a response lasts for a long time, it's probably hormonal. For example, when you get a shock, a hormone called adrenaline is released into the body (causing the fight or flight response, where your body is hyped up ready for action). You can tell it's a hormonal response (even though it kicks in pretty quickly) because you feel a bit wobbly for a while afterwards.

Testes — not quite as bad as examies...

Hormones control various organs and cells in the body, though they tend to control things that aren't immediately life-threatening (so things like sexual development, blood sugar level, etc.).

Q1   How do hormones travel to target cells? [1 mark]

Q2   What is an endocrine gland? [1 mark]

Controlling Blood Glucose

Your blood glucose level is kept nicely ticking over by two hormones — insulin and glucagon...

Insulin and Glucagon Control Blood Glucose Level

1) Eating foods containing carbohydrate puts glucose (a type of sugar) into the blood from the gut.
2) The normal metabolism of cells removes glucose from the blood.
3) Vigorous exercise removes much more glucose from the blood.
4) Excess glucose can be stored as glycogen in the liver and in the muscles.
5) The level of glucose in the blood must be kept steady. Changes are monitored and controlled by the pancreas, using the hormones insulin and glucagon.

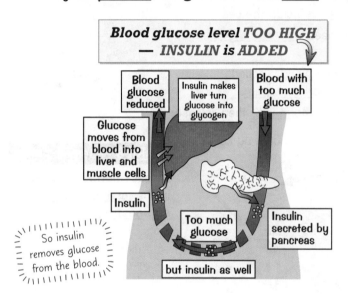

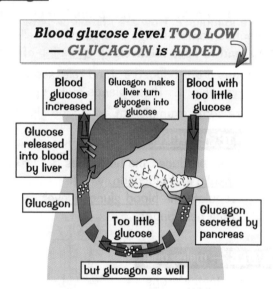

With Diabetes, You Can't Control Your Blood Glucose Level

Diabetes is a condition that affects your ability to control your blood glucose level. There are two types:

TYPE 1

1) Type 1 diabetes is where the pancreas produces little or no insulin.
2) This means a person's blood glucose level can rise to a level that can kill them.
3) People with Type 1 diabetes need insulin therapy — this usually involves several injections of insulin throughout the day, most likely at mealtimes. This makes sure that glucose is removed from the blood quickly once the food has been digested, stopping the level getting too high.
4) People with Type 1 diabetes also need to limit their intake of food rich in simple carbohydrates, e.g. sugars.

TYPE 2

1) Type 2 diabetes is where a person becomes resistant to their own insulin (they still produce insulin, but their body's cells don't respond properly to the hormone).
2) This can also cause a person's blood glucose level to rise to a dangerous level.
3) Type 2 diabetes can be controlled by eating a carbohydrate-controlled diet and getting regular exercise.

And people used to think the pancreas was just a cushion... (true)

This stuff can seem a bit confusing at first, but if you learn those two diagrams, it should get a bit easier.

Q1 Which organ is glucagon secreted from? [1 mark]

Q2 Describe how the blood glucose level is returned to normal when it is too high. [3 marks]

Revision Questions for Section 2b

Well, that's Section 2b done and dusted — I told you it was a corker. Time to check you've taken it all in...

- Try these questions and tick off each one when you get it right.
- When you've done all the questions for a topic and are completely happy with it, tick off the topic.

Nervous Control (p.36-38) ✓

1) What makes up the central nervous system and what does it do?
2) Produce a sketch of the brain and label the cerebrum, cerebellum and medulla.
3) Describe the structure of the cerebrum.
4) Give two things the medulla is responsible for.
5) What is a stimulus? How are stimuli detected?
6) How does information travel along neurons?
7) Give two types of effector.
8) Describe the role of an interneuron.
9) What is a synapse?
10) Explain why the transmission of nervous impulses is slowed down by synapses.
11) What is the purpose of a reflex action?
12) Describe the pathway of a reflex arc from stimulus to response.
13) Why are reflexes faster than normal nervous responses?

Hormonal Control (p.39-40) ✓

14) What is a hormone?
15) What is a target tissue?
16) Explain why hormones only affect certain cells.
17) Name two endocrine glands.
18) Give two differences between nervous and hormonal responses.
19) Where is excess glucose stored in the body?
20) What effect does the hormone glucagon have on blood glucose level?
21) A person with Type 2 diabetes doesn't respond properly to the insulin that they produce. Explain what effect this will have on their blood glucose level.

The Circulatory System

Multicellular organisms need transport systems to move substances around effectively. In animals, it's the job of the circulatory system. My heart's all of a flutter just thinking about it...

The DOUBLE Circulatory System, Actually

The circulatory system is made up of the heart, blood vessels and blood. Humans and other mammals have a double circulatory system — two circuits joined together:

1) In the first one, the heart pumps deoxygenated blood to the alveoli in the lungs to take in oxygen. The oxygenated blood then returns to the heart.

2) In the second one, the heart pumps oxygenated blood around all the other organs of the body (see right). Here, the blood gives up its oxygen at the body cells. The deoxygenated blood then returns to the heart to be pumped out to the lungs again.

3) As it is pumped around the body, the blood also travels through blood vessels near exchange surfaces — e.g. the villi (where it picks up food molecules, see p.46).

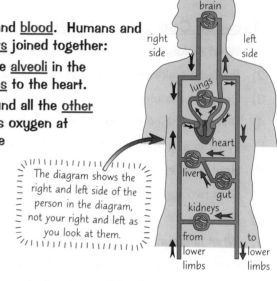

The diagram shows the right and left side of the person in the diagram, not your right and left as you look at them.

The Heart Pumps Blood Around The Body

1) The heart uses its four chambers (right and left atria and ventricles) to pump blood around.

2) The heart has valves to make sure that blood flows in the right direction. When the ventricles contract, the valves to the atria close and the valves to the blood vessels open. This prevents backflow (when the blood flows backwards).

1) Blood flows into the two atria from the vena cava and the pulmonary vein.

2) The atria contract, pushing the blood into the ventricles.

3) The ventricles contract, forcing the blood into the pulmonary artery and the aorta, and out of the heart.

4) The blood then flows to the organs, including the lungs, through arteries, and returns through veins (see next page).

5) The atria fill again and the whole cycle starts over.

Atria is plural. Atrium is when there is just one.

blue = deoxygenated blood
red = oxygenated blood

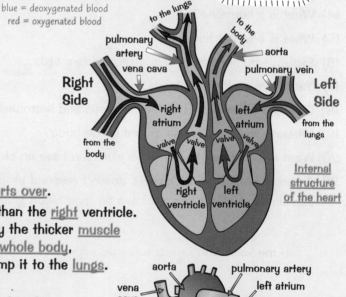

Internal structure of the heart

• The left ventricle has a much thicker wall than the right ventricle. It needs the greater pressure generated by the thicker muscle because it has to pump blood around the whole body, whereas the right ventricle only has to pump it to the lungs.

• The heart is made up of cardiac muscle. Cardiac muscle cells contain loads of mitochondria to provide them with ATP. This releases the energy needed for the muscle to contract.

• Blood is supplied to the cardiac muscle by two coronary arteries, which branch from the base of the aorta. They allow the oxygen and glucose needed for the heart cells to respire to diffuse through the thick walls of the heart.

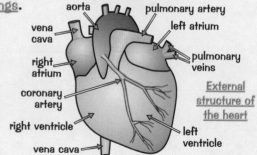

External structure of the heart

Okay — let's get to the heart of the matter...

Make sure you learn the names of the different parts of the heart and all the blood vessels that are attached to it.

Q1   Which chamber of the heart pumps deoxygenated blood to the lungs?   [1 mark]

The Blood Vessels

If you want to know more about the circulatory system you're in luck. Because here's a whole extra page.

Blood Vessels are Designed for Their Function

There are three main types of blood vessel:

1) **ARTERIES** — these carry the blood <u>away</u> from the heart.
2) **CAPILLARIES** — these are involved in the <u>exchange of materials</u> at the tissues.
3) **VEINS** — these carry the blood <u>to</u> the heart.

Arteries Carry Blood Under Pressure

1) The heart pumps the blood out at <u>high pressure</u> so the artery walls are <u>strong</u> and <u>elastic</u>.

2) The walls are <u>thick</u> compared to the size of the central channel.

3) They contain thick layers of <u>muscle</u> to make them <u>strong</u>, and <u>elastic fibres</u> to allow them to stretch and <u>spring back</u>.

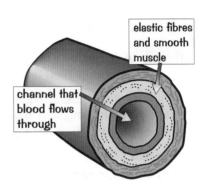

elastic fibres and smooth muscle

channel that blood flows through

Capillaries are Really Small

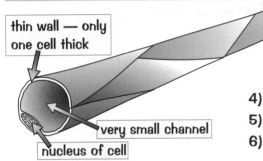

thin wall — only one cell thick

very small channel

nucleus of cell

1) Arteries branch into <u>capillaries</u>.

2) Capillaries are really <u>tiny</u> — too small to see.

3) They form large <u>networks</u> that <u>spread</u> through tissues and organs. This means they can carry the blood <u>really close</u> to <u>every cell</u> in the body to <u>exchange substances</u> with them.

4) They have <u>permeable</u> walls, so substances can <u>diffuse</u> in and out.

5) They supply <u>food</u> and <u>oxygen</u>, and take away <u>waste</u> like CO_2.

6) Their walls are usually <u>only one cell thick</u>. This <u>increases</u> the rate of diffusion by <u>decreasing</u> the <u>distance</u> over which it occurs.

7) Capillaries have a <u>large surface area</u>, which also <u>increases</u> the rate of diffusion of substances.

Veins Take Blood Back to the Heart

1) Capillaries eventually <u>join up</u> to form <u>veins</u>.

2) The blood is at <u>lower pressure</u> in the veins so the walls don't need to be as <u>thick</u> as artery walls.

3) They have a <u>bigger central channel</u> than arteries to help the blood <u>flow</u> despite the lower pressure.

4) Unlike arteries and capillaries, they have <u>valves</u> to help keep the blood flowing in the <u>right direction</u>.

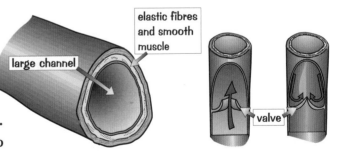

elastic fibres and smooth muscle

large channel

valve

Learn this page — don't struggle in vein...

Here's an interesting fact for you — your body contains about 60 000 miles of blood vessels. That's about six times the distance from Edinburgh to Sydney in Australia. Of course, capillaries are really tiny, which is how such a massive amount of them can fit in your body — they can only be seen with a microscope.

Q1 Describe how veins are adapted to carry blood back to the heart. [2 marks]

Q2 Explain how capillaries are adapted to their function. [4 marks]

The Blood

Now that we've looked at blood vessels, it's time to look at the wonders of <u>blood</u> itself.
(Hmmm — is it me, or is this starting to sound a tiny bit like a lecture for <u>vampires</u>...)

Blood Acts as a Transport System

1) One of blood's jobs is to act as a huge <u>transport system</u> — it delivers substances around the body.

2) Blood is a <u>tissue</u>, consisting of many similar cells working together.

3) These cells include <u>red blood cells</u> and <u>white blood cells</u>. They're suspended in a liquid called <u>plasma</u>.

Red Blood Cells Carry Oxygen

1) The job of red blood cells is to carry <u>oxygen</u> from the lungs to all the cells in the body. They are <u>specialised</u> for this <u>job</u> in several ways.

2) They have a <u>biconcave disc</u> shape (in other words, they look a bit like a jam doughnut that's being pressed in at the top and bottom) to give a <u>large surface area</u> for absorbing <u>oxygen</u>.

3) They <u>don't</u> have a nucleus — this allows more <u>room</u> to carry oxygen.

4) They contain a red pigment called <u>haemoglobin</u>, which contains iron.

5) In the <u>lungs</u>, haemoglobin binds to <u>oxygen</u> to become <u>oxyhaemoglobin</u>.

oxygen + haemoglobin ⟶ oxyhaemoglobin

6) In body tissues, the reverse happens — oxyhaemoglobin splits up into haemoglobin and oxygen, to <u>release oxygen</u> to the <u>cells</u>.

White Blood Cells Defend Against Infection

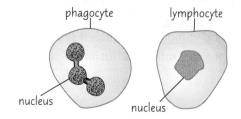

phagocyte   lymphocyte

nucleus   nucleus

1) The main job of <u>white blood cells</u> is <u>fighting disease</u>.

2) There are a few <u>different types</u> of white blood cells — you need to know about the main ones involved in fighting disease — <u>phagocytes</u> and <u>lymphocytes</u> (see next page).

Unlike red blood cells, white blood cells do have a nucleus.

Plasma is the Liquid That Carries Everything in Blood

Plasma is a pale straw-coloured liquid. It <u>carries just about everything</u> including:

1) <u>Red</u> and <u>white blood cells</u>.

2) Nutrients like <u>glucose</u> and <u>amino acids</u>. These are the soluble products of digestion which are absorbed from the gut and taken to the cells of the body.

3) <u>Hormones</u> — these act like chemical messengers — see p.39.

4) <u>Carbon dioxide</u> from the organs to the lungs.

5) <u>Antibodies</u> produced by the white blood cells (see next page).

Red blood cells — it's embarrassing to have no nucleus...

When you're ill the doctor often takes a blood sample for analysis. Blood tests can be used to diagnose loads of things — not just disorders of the blood. This is because the blood transports so many chemicals produced by so many organs... and it's easier to take blood than, say, a piece of muscle.

Q1   Give the product of the binding of oxygen and haemoglobin.

[1 mark]

The Immune System

Your <u>white blood cells</u> have some pretty neat tricks up their sleeves when it comes to <u>fighting disease</u>...

Pathogens Cause Disease

1) Pathogens are micro-organisms that <u>cause diseases</u>.
   Pathogens include micro-organisms like <u>bacteria</u>, <u>fungi</u> and <u>viruses</u>.

2) Your body is pretty good at <u>stopping</u> pathogens from <u>getting in</u>. However, if they do manage to make it into your body, your <u>immune system</u> kicks in to destroy them...

> Not all micro-organisms cause disease. For example, many bacteria carry out important functions in the body.

Your Immune System Can Attack Pathogens

The most important part of your <u>immune system</u> is the <u>white blood cells</u>. They travel around in your <u>blood</u> and crawl into every part of you, constantly patrolling for <u>pathogens</u>. As you saw on the previous page, there are <u>two types</u> of <u>white blood cell</u> that you need to know about — <u>phagocytes</u> and <u>lymphocytes</u>.

Phagocytes Consume Invading Pathogens

<u>Phagocytes</u> have a <u>flexible membrane</u> and contain lots of <u>enzymes</u>. This enables them to <u>engulf</u> foreign cells and <u>digest</u> them. This is called <u>phagocytosis</u>.

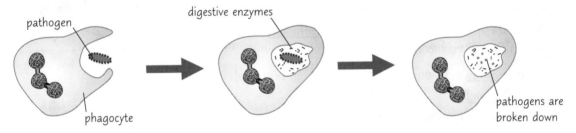

Lymphocytes Produce Antibodies Against Invading Pathogens

1) Every invading pathogen has unique molecules (<u>antigens</u>) on its surface.

2) When some of your lymphocytes come across a <u>foreign antigen</u> (i.e. one they don't recognise), they will start to produce <u>proteins</u> called <u>antibodies</u> to lock onto the invading cells. The antibodies produced are <u>specific</u> to that type of antigen — they won't lock on to any others.

3) Antibodies are then produced <u>rapidly</u> and carried around the body to <u>lock on</u> to all similar pathogens.

4) The <u>antibodies</u> may <u>disable</u> the pathogen or 'tag' the pathogens, which <u>helps</u> the phagocytes <u>find</u> them so they can <u>engulf</u> them.

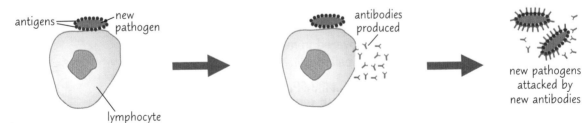

5) Some special lymphocytes, called <u>memory cells</u>, <u>stay around</u> in the blood after the pathogen has been fought off. If the person is <u>infected</u> with the <u>same</u> <u>pathogen again</u>, the white blood cells will rapidly produce the antibodies to help destroy it — the person is <u>naturally</u> immune to that pathogen and won't get ill.

Fight disease — give your nose a blow with boxing gloves...

The <u>body</u> makes <u>antibodies</u> against the <u>antigens</u> on <u>pathogens</u>. There, don't say I never help you. Right, tea...

Q1   Describe the role of phagocytes in the defence of the body against pathogens.   [1 mark]

Exchanging Materials

Back to transporting substances now — substances need delivering to cells, and waste products need removing from them. Exchange surfaces are adapted so that these substances can move through them efficiently...

Exchange Surfaces have Adaptations to Increase the Efficiency of Absorption

Exchange surfaces are adapted to maximise effectiveness:

- They are thin, so substances only have a short distance to travel.
- They have a large surface area, so lots of a substance can move at once.
- Exchange surfaces in animals have lots of blood vessels, to get stuff into and out of the blood quickly.

Here are two examples of exchange surfaces you need to know about. First up, the alveoli...

Gas Exchange Happens in the Lungs

Remember, cells need oxygen for aerobic respiration and produce carbon dioxide as a waste product (see p.18).

1) The lungs transfer oxygen (O_2) to the blood, so that it can be transported to cells. The lungs also remove waste carbon dioxide (CO_2) from the blood.

2) To do this the lungs contain millions of little air sacs called alveoli surrounded by a network of capillaries. This is where gas exchange takes place.

3) The alveoli are specialised to maximise the diffusion of O_2 and CO_2. They have:

- An enormous surface area (about 75 m² in humans).
- Very thin walls.
- A network of capillaries surrounding them.

4) The blood passing next to the alveoli has just returned to the lungs from the rest of the body via the heart (see p.42), so it contains lots of CO_2 and very little O_2.

5) At this point, CO_2 moves out of the blood into the alveolus and O_2 moves out of the alveolus into the blood by diffusion — see page 16).

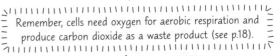

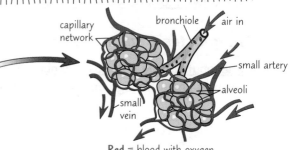
Red = blood with oxygen.
Blue = blood with carbon dioxide.

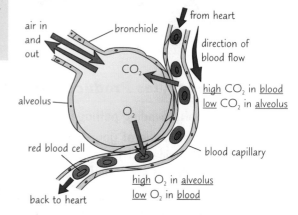
high CO_2 in blood
low CO_2 in alveolus

high O_2 in alveolus
low O_2 in blood

The Villi Provide a Really Big Surface Area

1) The small intestine is where dissolved food molecules are absorbed out of the digestive system and into the blood so that they can be delivered to cells.

2) The inside of the small intestine is covered in millions and millions of tiny little projections called villi.

3) They increase the surface area in a big way so that dissolved food molecules are absorbed from the gut much more quickly. They also have thin walls to speed up absorption.

4) Inside each villus is a network of capillaries for absorbing glucose and amino acids, and a lacteal for absorbing the products of fat digestion — fatty acids and glycerol.

Cells use dissolved food molecules such as glucose for respiration.

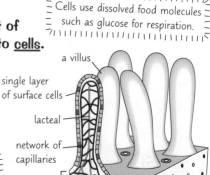

The products of fat digestion can't be absorbed directly into the blood so they're absorbed by the lacteal and delivered to the blood elsewhere in the body.

Al Veoli — the Italian gas man...

Don't turn over 'til you've learnt exactly how these specialised surfaces help to maximise absorption.

Q1 Explain why it is beneficial for an exchange surface to be just one cell thick. [1 mark]

Plant Structure

It's not just animals that need to transport and exchange substances — plants are in on the act too.

Plant Cells Are Organised Into Tissues And Organs

See p.30 for more on cell organisation.

Plants are made of organs like stems, roots and leaves. Plant organs work together to make organ systems. These can perform the various tasks that a plant needs to carry out to survive and grow — for example, transporting substances around the plant. Plant organs are made of tissues. Examples of plant tissues are:

1) Epidermal tissue — this covers the whole plant.

2) Palisade mesophyll tissue — this is the part of the leaf where most photosynthesis happens.

3) Spongy mesophyll tissue — this is also in the leaf, and contains big air spaces to allow gases to diffuse in and out of cells.

For more on photosynthesis, see page 52.

> When plants photosynthesise they use up CO CO_2 from the atmosphere and produce O_2 as a waste product. When plants respire they use up O_2 and produce CO_2 as a waste product. So there are lots of gases moving to and fro in plants, and this movement happens by diffusion. Water vapour also diffuses out of the leaf — see p.49.

For more on respiration, see p.18-19.

4) Xylem and phloem — they transport things like water, mineral ions and sugar around the plant (through the roots, stems and leaves — see next page).

5) Meristem tissue — this is found at the growing tips of shoots and roots and is able to divide and form lots of different types of plant cell, allowing the plant to grow.

A merry stem.

The Leaf is an Organ Made Up of Several Types of Tissue

Leaves contain epidermal, mesophyll, xylem and phloem tissues.

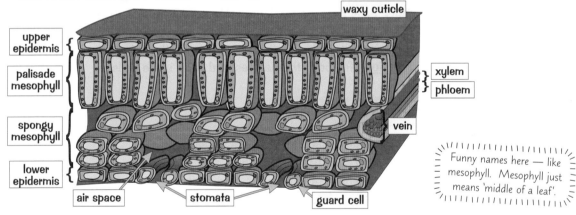

Labels: waxy cuticle, upper epidermis, palisade mesophyll, spongy mesophyll, lower epidermis, xylem, phloem, vein, air space, stomata, guard cell

Funny names here — like mesophyll. Mesophyll just means 'middle of a leaf'.

The structures of the tissues that make up the leaf are related to their function:

1) The epidermal tissues are covered with a waxy cuticle, which helps to reduce water loss by evaporation.

2) The upper epidermis is transparent so that light can pass through it to the palisade layer.

3) The palisade layer has lots of chloroplasts (the little structures where photosynthesis takes place). This means that they're near the top of the leaf where they can get the most light.

4) The xylem and phloem (found in the vein) deliver water and other nutrients to the entire leaf and take away the sugar produced by photosynthesis. They also help support the structure of the leaf.

5) The tissues of leaves are also adapted for efficient gas exchange. E.g. the lower epidermis is full of little holes called stomata, which let gases diffuse directly into and out of the leaf. The opening and closing of stomata is controlled by guard cells in response to environmental conditions (see p.49). The air spaces in the spongy mesophyll tissue increase the rate of diffusion of gases.

Plant cell organisation — millions of members worldwide...

There are a lot of weird names here, so make sure you spend plenty of time on this page. Maybe you could draw your own leaf diagram and label it with descriptions of the different tissue types.

Q1   Name two plant organs.   [2 marks]

Transport in Plants

So plants get stuff from <u>A to B</u> via <u>xylem</u> and <u>phloem</u>. Both types of vessel go to <u>every part</u> of the plant, but they're totally <u>separate</u>. The <u>roots</u> are involved in transport too, as they get stuff into the plant in the first place.

Root Hairs Take In Minerals and Water

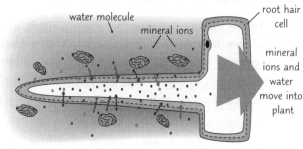

water molecule
mineral ions
root hair cell
mineral ions and water move into plant

1) The cells on the surface of plant roots grow into "<u>hairs</u>", which stick out into the soil.

2) Each branch of a root will be covered in <u>millions</u> of these microscopic root hairs.

3) This gives the plant a <u>large surface area</u> for absorbing <u>water</u> and <u>mineral ions</u> from the soil.

4) The concentration of mineral ions is usually <u>higher</u> in the <u>root hair cells</u> than in the <u>soil</u> around them, so mineral ions are absorbed by <u>active transport</u> (see page 17). Water is absorbed by <u>osmosis</u> (see p.17).

Sugar

Phloem Vessels Transport Sugar

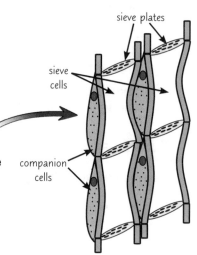

sieve plates
sieve cells
companion cells

1) Phloem vessels transport <u>sugar</u> made in the leaves to the rest of the plant for <u>immediate use</u> (e.g. in growing regions) or for <u>storage</u>.

2) The <u>transport</u> goes in <u>both directions</u>.

3) Phloem vessels are made of columns of <u>elongated living cells</u> called <u>sieve cells</u>. At the top and bottom of each of the sieve cells is a <u>sieve plate</u>. These have <u>small pores</u> in them to allow stuff to pass through.

4) Sieve cells have <u>no nucleus</u>. This means that they <u>can't survive</u> on their own, so each sieve cell has a <u>companion cell</u>. These cells carry out the <u>living functions</u> for both themselves and their sieve cells.

Xylem Vessels Take Water UP

Water and minerals

1) Xylem vessels carry <u>water</u> and <u>mineral ions</u> from the <u>roots</u> to the <u>stem</u> and <u>leaves</u>.

2) The movement of water <u>from</u> the <u>roots</u>, <u>through</u> the <u>xylem</u> and <u>out</u> of the <u>leaves</u> is called the <u>transpiration stream</u> (see next page).

3) Xylem vessels are made of <u>dead cells</u> joined end to end with <u>no</u> end walls between them and a hole down the middle.

4) Xylem cells are <u>lignified</u> — they're <u>strengthened</u> with a material called <u>lignin</u>, which spirals up the inside of the xylem. This extra strength allows xylem to withstand changes in <u>pressure</u> as water moves through it.

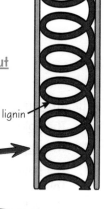

lignin

You can use a <u>light microscope</u> to observe the <u>structure</u> of <u>xylem</u> and <u>phloem</u> in <u>thin sections</u> of a plant's stem. If the stem is left upright in a beaker of <u>eosin dye</u>, the dye will travel up the stem, staining the <u>xylem</u> red. A thin section of the stem can then be taken and viewed on a slide under a microscope.

PRACTICAL

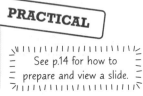

See p.14 for how to prepare and view a slide.

Don't let revision stress you out — just go with the phloem...

Phl<u>o</u>em transports substances in b<u>o</u>th directions, but xylem only transports things upwards — x<u>y</u> to the sky.

Q1 Describe the function of the phloem vessels. [2 marks]

Q2 Explain why xylem vessels are lignified. [2 marks]

Transpiration

Next up, transpiration. If you think revision is thirsty work, try being a plant...

Transpiration is the Loss of Water from the Plant

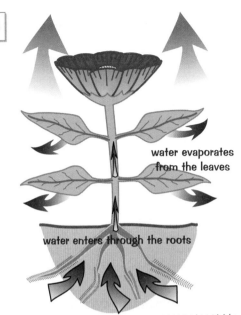

water evaporates from the leaves

water enters through the roots

1) Transpiration is caused by the evaporation and diffusion (see p.16) of water from a plant's surface.
Water diffuses out through the stomata (tiny pores on the surface of the plant). Most transpiration happens at the leaves because that's where most of the stomata are found.

2) The loss of water creates a slight shortage of water in the leaf, and so more water is drawn up from the rest of the plant through the xylem vessels to replace it.

3) This in turn means more water is drawn up from the roots by osmosis, and so there's a constant transpiration stream of water through the plant.

4) The transpiration stream carries mineral ions that are dissolved in the water along with it.

Stomata are mainly found in the lower epidermis of the leaf (see p.47).

Stomata Open and Close Automatically

Stomata are able to open and close to control the amount of water lost from the leaves.

1) Stomata are surrounded by guard cells, which change shape to control the size of the pore.

2) When the guard cells are turgid (swollen with water) the stomata are open, and when the guard cells are flaccid (low on water and limp) the stomata are closed.

3) Stomata close automatically when supplies of water start to dry up — they're also sensitive to light and close at night to save water without losing out on photosynthesis.

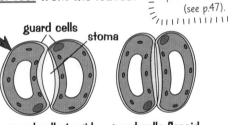

guard cells   stoma

guard cells turgid — stoma open   guard cells flaccid — stoma closed

You Can View Stomata Under a Microscope   PRACTICAL

Stomata can be observed using a light microscope. You can prepare a slide to view them on using the following (ridiculously easy) method:

1) Paint two thin layers of clear nail varnish onto the leaf you want to look at. Leave the varnish to dry in between each coat.

2) Put a piece of clear sticky tape over the top of the painted leaf and use it to peel the varnish off slowly. The varnish will have an impression of the leaf's surface.

3) Stick the tape with the varnish onto a microscope slide.

You can then view your slide under the microscope (see p.14 for how to do this). You should be able to count the stomata and guard cells from the impression on the varnish. If you compare the top and bottom surfaces of a leaf you should find that there are more stomata on the bottom of the leaf.

I say stomaaarta, you say stomaaayta...

A tree can lose around 1000 litres of water from its leaves every day. That's about as much water as the average person drinks in a year. No wonder the stomata close when the soil's dry or it's too dark to photosynthesise.

Q1   Name the part of the plant where the majority of stomata are located.   [1 mark]

Q2   Explain how water moves through a plant via the process of transpiration.   [3 marks]

Transpiration Rate

If you thought that stuff on <u>transpiration</u> was interesting, you're in luck — here's another page all about it...

Transpiration Rate is Affected by Four Main Things

1) <u>SURFACE AREA</u> — the <u>greater</u> the <u>surface area</u> of the <u>leaves</u>, the <u>greater</u> the transpiration rate.

   A greater surface area means more stomata for water to escape from.

2) <u>TEMPERATURE</u> — the <u>warmer</u> it is, the <u>faster</u> transpiration happens.

   When it's warm the water particles have more energy to evaporate and diffuse out of the stomata.

3) <u>WIND SPEED</u> — the <u>faster</u> the <u>wind speed</u> around a leaf, the <u>greater</u> the transpiration rate.

   If air flow around a leaf is poor (low wind speed), the water vapour just surrounds the leaf and doesn't move away. This means there's a high concentration of water particles outside the leaf as well as inside it, so diffusion doesn't happen as quickly. If there's good air flow (high wind speed), the water vapour is swept away, so diffusion happens quickly.

4) <u>HUMIDITY</u> — the <u>drier</u> the air around a leaf, the <u>faster</u> transpiration happens.

   This is like what happens with wind speed. If the air is humid there's a lot of water in it already, so there's not much of a difference between the inside and the outside of the leaf. Diffusion happens fastest if there's a really high concentration in one place, and a really low concentration in the other.

A Potometer can be Used to Estimate Transpiration Rate

PRACTICAL

A <u>potometer</u> is a special piece of apparatus used to <u>estimate transpiration rate</u>. It actually <u>measures water uptake</u> by a plant, but it's <u>assumed</u> that water uptake by the plant is <u>directly related</u> to water loss from the leaves (transpiration). Here's how to use a potometer:

1) <u>Cut</u> a shoot <u>underwater</u> to prevent air from entering the xylem.
   Cut it at a <u>slant</u> to increase the surface area available for water uptake.

2) <u>Assemble</u> the potometer <u>in water</u> and insert the shoot <u>under water</u>, so no <u>air</u> can enter.

3) Remove the apparatus from the water but keep the end of the capillary tube <u>submerged</u> in a beaker of water.

4) Check that the apparatus is <u>watertight</u> and <u>airtight</u>.

5) <u>Dry</u> the leaves, allow time for the shoot to <u>acclimatise</u> and then <u>shut</u> the tap.

6) Remove the end of the capillary tube from the beaker of water until <u>one air bubble</u> has formed, then put the end of the tube <u>back into the water</u>.

7) Record the <u>starting position</u> of the air bubble.

8) Start a <u>stopwatch</u> and record the <u>distance moved</u> by the bubble per unit time, e.g. per hour. Calculating the <u>speed</u> of <u>air bubble movement</u> allows you to <u>measure water uptake</u>.

9) Keep the <u>conditions constant</u> throughout the experiment, e.g. the <u>temperature</u> and <u>air humidity</u>.

reservoir of water

Tap is shut off during experiment.

As the plant takes up water, the air bubble moves along the scale.

Water moves this way.

capillary tube with a scale

Bubble moves this way.

beaker of water

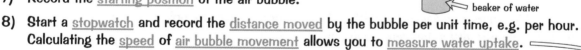

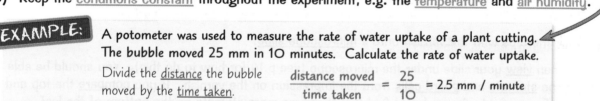

EXAMPLE: A potometer was used to measure the rate of water uptake of a plant cutting. The bubble moved 25 mm in 10 minutes. Calculate the rate of water uptake.

Divide the <u>distance</u> the bubble moved by the <u>time taken</u>.

$$\frac{\text{distance moved}}{\text{time taken}} = \frac{25}{10} = 2.5 \text{ mm / minute}$$

10) To investigate how different factors <u>affect</u> the <u>rate</u> of water uptake use the setup above as a control. Next, vary an <u>environmental condition</u> — e.g. use a fan to increase the air movement around the plant — and run the experiment <u>again</u>. Then <u>compare</u> the results to the <u>control</u>.

Potometer — a surprisingly useless tool for measuring crockery...

The tricky bit of using a potometer is setting it up — keeping air out and water in is harder than it sounds.

Q1   Give three factors that affect the rate of transpiration in plants.

[3 marks]

Revision Questions for Section 2c

Well, that wraps up <u>Section 2c</u> — now for a few quick-fire questions to get your blood pumping.
* Try these questions and <u>tick off each one</u> when you <u>get it right</u>.
* When you've done <u>all the questions</u> for a topic and are <u>completely happy</u> with it, tick off the topic.

The Circulatory System and Blood Vessels (p.42-43) ☑
1) Explain why the circulatory system in humans is described as a 'double circulatory system'.
2) Name the four chambers of the heart.
3) Name the blood vessel that transports blood from the heart to the rest of the body.
4) Is blood in the pulmonary artery oxygenated or deoxygenated?
5) Which type of blood vessel carries blood at high pressure?
6) Describe the role of capillaries.
7) True or False? Veins have thick muscular walls.
8) Describe the role of valves in blood vessels.

The Blood (p.44-45) ☐
9) Why don't red blood cells have a nucleus?
10) Name two types of white blood cell.
11) Name four substances that are found in blood plasma.
12) What is a pathogen?
13) What type of white blood cell produces antibodies?
14) Explain how the production of antibodies helps the body defend itself against disease.

Exchanging Materials (p.46) ☐
15) What gases are exchanged at the alveoli?
16) Give three ways that alveoli are adapted for efficient gas exchange.
17) Other than alveoli, give an example of a specialised exchange surface found in an animal.
18) What is absorbed by the lacteal?

Plant Structure, Plant Transport and Transpiration (p.47-50) ☐
19) List three tissues found in a leaf.
20) Give two substances that a plant takes in via its root hairs.
21) True or False? Substances transported in the phloem can move in both directions.
22) Which type of plant transport vessel contains sieve tube elements?
23) What is a companion cell?
24) What do xylem vessels transport?
25) Which type of plant transport vessel is made up of dead cells?
26) What is transpiration?
27) What effect would an increase in humidity have on the rate of transpiration?
28) How could you estimate the rate of transpiration?

Photosynthesis

Plants are able to get all the energy they need from the sun — it sounds great, no need to cook ever again...

Photosynthesis Produces Sugar Using Light Energy

1) Photosynthesis uses energy to change carbon dioxide (CO_2) and water into sugar and oxygen.

The sugar made in photosynthesis is glucose.

2) It takes place in chloroplasts in green plant cells. Chloroplasts contain chlorophyll — a pigment that traps light energy from the sun.

3) The word summary for photosynthesis is:

$$\text{carbon dioxide} + \text{water} \xrightarrow{\text{light energy}} \text{sugar} + \text{oxygen}$$

Photosynthesis Can be Split into Two Stages

Stage 1 — Light Reactions

1) This stage can only happen when light is available.

2) Chlorophyll in chloroplasts traps light energy entering the cell.

3) The light energy is then converted into chemical energy.

4) The chemical energy is used to make ATP, which is then used in the second stage of photosynthesis.

5) During these reactions, water is split into oxygen and hydrogen.

6) Oxygen diffuses out of the cell, while hydrogen stays in the cell to be used in the second stage of photosynthesis.

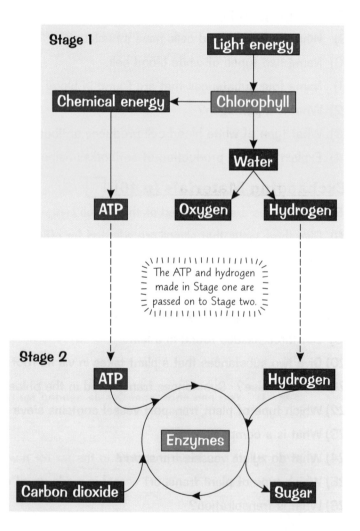
The ATP and hydrogen made in Stage one are passed on to Stage two.

Stage 2 — Carbon Fixation

1) This stage doesn't need light but it still needs energy. Energy is provided by releasing the chemical energy in ATP from the first stage of photosynthesis.

2) Hydrogen and carbon dioxide are combined in a series of reactions to produce sugar.

3) The reactions are controlled by enzymes.

You are my sunshine, my only sunshine, you make me happy...

...when skies are grey. The oxygen that's produced in photosynthesis is the oxygen that me, you and your dog are all breathing in right now. So next time you see a tree, don't forget to thank it for all the lovely oxygen.

Q1   Describe the role of chlorophyll in photosynthesis.   [1 mark]

Q2   Name the two substances formed when water is split during photosynthesis.   [1 mark]

More on Photosynthesis

The previous page was all about how plants <u>produce</u> sugar, but now you need to know what they <u>do with it</u> all.

Plants Use Sugar in Three Main Ways...

1) <u>For respiration</u> — This <u>releases</u> the <u>chemical energy</u> that's stored in sugar, which is used for many <u>essential processes</u> in the plant.

See p.18 for more on respiration.

2) <u>Making cellulose</u> — Sugar is converted into <u>cellulose</u> — an important <u>structural material</u> in <u>plant cell walls</u> (see p.13).

3) <u>Stored as starch</u> — Sugar is turned into <u>starch</u> and <u>stored</u> in roots, stems and leaves. Starch can be used for <u>energy</u> when photosynthesis isn't happening (e.g. in winter when a plant may lose all of its leaves).

You Can Investigate What is Needed for Photosynthesis PRACTICAL

1) The presence of <u>starch</u> is really easy to <u>test</u> for, which means there are simple <u>experiments</u> you can do to find out if a plant has been <u>photosynthesising</u> (as if a plant can't photosynthesise, it can't make starch).

2) This is how you can <u>test</u> for the <u>presence</u> of starch in a <u>leaf</u>:

> 1) Start by dunking the leaf in boiling water (hold it with tweezers or forceps). This <u>stops</u> any <u>chemical reactions</u> happening inside the leaf.
>
> 2) Now put the leaf in a boiling tube with some <u>ethanol</u> and heat it in an electric water bath until it boils — this gets rid of any <u>chlorophyll</u> and makes the leaf a <u>white-ish</u> colour.
>
> Ethanol is highly flammable — keep it away from naked flames, e.g. Bunsen burners.
>
> 3) Finally, <u>rinse</u> the leaf in <u>cold water</u> and add a few drops of <u>iodine solution</u> — if <u>starch</u> is <u>present</u> the leaf will turn <u>blue-black</u>. If starch is <u>absent</u> the leaf will go <u>yellow/orange</u> because the brown iodine solution stains it.
>
>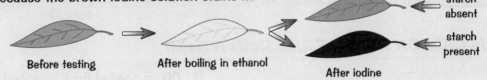
>
> Before testing   After boiling in ethanol   starch absent   starch present   After iodine

3) The starch test above can be used to show <u>what's needed</u> for photosynthesis to take place. For example, you can do these experiments to show that <u>light</u> and <u>CO$_2$</u> are needed:

> **Light**
> 1) Grow a plant in the <u>dark</u> (e.g. in a cupboard) for <u>48 hours</u>. Growing it for this long gives the plant chance to <u>use up</u> any <u>stored starch</u> it has in its leaves.
> 2) Then <u>test</u> one of its leaves for starch — it <u>won't</u> turn blue-black.
> 3) This shows that <u>no starch</u> is <u>made</u> in the <u>dark</u>, showing that <u>light is needed</u> for photosynthesis.

> **Carbon Dioxide**
> 1) You can show that <u>CO$_2$</u> is needed for photosynthesis with the apparatus shown on the right.
> 2) The soda lime will <u>absorb CO$_2$</u> out of the air in the jar.
> 3) If you leave the plant in the jar for a while and then <u>test</u> a leaf for starch, it <u>won't</u> turn blue-black.
> 4) This shows that <u>no starch</u> has been made in the leaf, which means that <u>CO$_2$ is needed</u> for photosynthesis.
>
>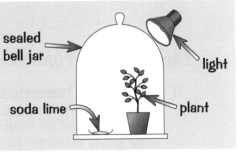
>
> sealed bell jar   light   soda lime   plant

It's important to <u>control</u> the <u>temperature</u> in these tests. That way you know photosynthesis was prevented by lack of <u>light</u> or <u>CO$_2$</u> and <u>not</u> by the <u>temperature</u> being <u>too high</u> or <u>too low</u> (see next page).

A spoonful of sugar, helps the cellulose get made...

I use sugar to bake brownies, but you don't need to know that — you need to know what plants do with sugar.

Q1   Name one substance that a plant converts sugar into.   [1 mark]

The Rate of Photosynthesis

Okey dokey — it's time to find out how <u>light</u>, <u>CO_2</u> and <u>temperature</u> affect the <u>rate of photosynthesis</u>. Coming up are a load of <u>lovely pictures</u> (well... graphs) and a <u>smasher</u> of an <u>experiment</u> to finish off.

The Rate of Photosynthesis is Influenced by Different Factors

1) How <u>fast</u> a plant can photosynthesise <u>affects</u> its <u>growth</u>. This is largely because the <u>sugar</u> made during photosynthesis is needed for <u>respiration</u>, which releases the energy needed for processes that make the plant <u>grow</u> (e.g. cell division and protein synthesis).

2) So the <u>faster</u> the <u>rate of photosynthesis</u>, the <u>faster</u> a plant can <u>grow</u>.

3) The rate of photosynthesis can be affected by <u>light intensity</u>, <u>concentration of CO_2</u> and <u>temperature</u>. Any of these can become <u>limiting factors</u>, meaning they can <u>stop</u> photosynthesis from happening <u>any faster</u>.

4) You need to be able to <u>interpret graphs</u> showing <u>how</u> each of these <u>factors</u> can <u>affect</u> the <u>rate of photosynthesis</u>.

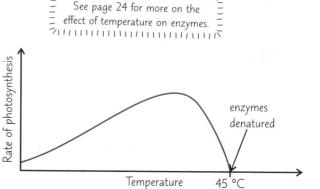

Not Enough LIGHT Slows Down the Rate of Photosynthesis

1) <u>Light energy</u> is needed for photosynthesis.

2) As the <u>light level</u> is raised, the rate of photosynthesis <u>increases steadily</u> — but only up to a <u>certain point</u>.

3) Beyond that, it <u>won't</u> make any difference — it'll be either the <u>temperature</u> or the <u>CO_2 concentration</u> which is the limiting factor.

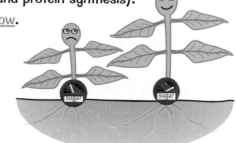

CO_2 or temp needs to be increased

rate increases with light intensity

Rate of photosynthesis

Light intensity

Too Little CARBON DIOXIDE Also Slows it Down

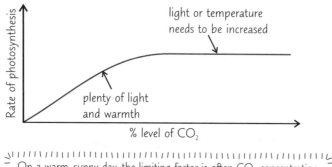

light or temperature needs to be increased

plenty of light and warmth

Rate of photosynthesis

% level of CO_2

On a warm, sunny day, the limiting factor is often CO_2 concentration.

1) <u>CO_2</u> is <u>needed</u> for the <u>second stage</u> of <u>photosynthesis</u> (see p.52).

2) This means that <u>increasing the concentration of CO_2</u> will increase the rate of photosynthesis — but only up to a point. After this the graph <u>flattens out</u> — CO_2 is no longer the <u>limiting factor</u>.

3) If <u>CO_2</u> is in plentiful supply, then the factor limiting photosynthesis must be <u>light</u> or <u>temperature</u>.

The TEMPERATURE has to be Just Right

1) Usually, if the <u>temperature</u> is the <u>limiting factor</u> it's because it's <u>too low</u> — the <u>enzymes</u> needed for photosynthesis work more <u>slowly</u> at low temperatures.

2) But if the plant gets <u>too hot</u>, the enzymes it needs for photosynthesis and its other reactions will be <u>denatured</u> — the <u>rate</u> of reaction <u>decreases</u> dramatically.

3) This happens at about <u>45 °C</u> (pretty hot for outdoors, but <u>greenhouses</u> can get that hot if you're not careful).

See page 24 for more on the effect of temperature on enzymes.

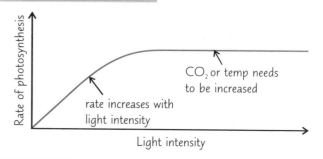

enzymes denatured

Rate of photosynthesis

Temperature   45 °C

The Rate of Photosynthesis

One Graph May Show the Effect of Many Limiting Factors

You could get a graph that shows <u>more than one</u> limiting factor on the rate of photosynthesis, for example:

1) The graph on the right shows how the rate of photosynthesis is affected by <u>light intensity</u> and <u>temperature</u>.

2) At the start, both of the lines show that as the light intensity <u>increases</u>, the rate of photosynthesis <u>increases steadily</u>.

3) But the lines <u>level off</u> when <u>light</u> is <u>no longer</u> the limiting factor. The line at <u>25 °C</u> levels off at a <u>higher point</u> than the one at 15 °C, showing that <u>temperature</u> must have been a <u>limiting factor</u> at 15 °C.

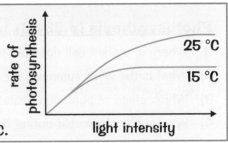

1) The graph on the right shows how the rate of photosynthesis is affected by <u>light intensity</u> and <u>CO_2 concentration</u>.

2) Again, both the lines <u>level off</u> when <u>light</u> is <u>no longer</u> the limiting factor.

3) The line at the <u>higher CO_2 concentration of 0.4%</u> levels off at a <u>higher point</u> than the one at 0.04%. This means <u>CO_2 concentration</u> must have been a <u>limiting factor</u> at 0.04% CO_2. The limiting factor here <u>isn't temperature</u> because it's the <u>same</u> for both lines (25 °C).

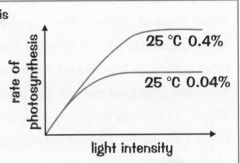

Oxygen Production Shows the Rate of Photosynthesis | PRACTICAL

Some types of <u>pondweed</u> can be used to measure the effect of different factors on the <u>rate of photosynthesis</u>. The rate at which the pondweed produces <u>oxygen</u> corresponds to the rate at which it's photosynthesising — the <u>faster</u> the rate of oxygen production, the <u>faster</u> the rate of photosynthesis. Here's how you can investigate the effect of <u>light intensity</u>:

1) A source of <u>white light</u> is placed at a <u>specific distance</u> from the pondweed.

2) The pondweed is left to photosynthesise for a <u>set amount of time</u>. As it photosynthesises, the oxygen released will collect in the <u>capillary tube</u>.

3) At the end of the experiment, the <u>syringe</u> is used to draw the gas bubble in the tube up alongside a ruler and the <u>length</u> of the <u>gas bubble</u> is <u>measured</u>. This is <u>proportional</u> to the <u>volume of O_2</u> produced.

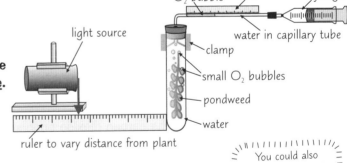

4) For this experiment, any <u>variables</u> that could affect the results should be <u>controlled</u>, e.g. the <u>temperature</u> and <u>time</u> the pondweed is left to photosynthesise.

5) The experiment is <u>repeated</u> twice with the <u>light source</u> at the <u>same</u> distance and the <u>mean</u> volume of O_2 produced is calculated.

6) Then the whole experiment is repeated with the <u>light source</u> at <u>different distances</u> from the pondweed.

The apparatus above can be altered to measure the effect of <u>temperature</u> or <u>CO_2</u> on photosynthesis. E.g. the test tube of pondweed can be put into a <u>water bath</u> at a <u>set temperature</u>, or a measured amount of <u>sodium hydrogencarbonate</u> can be dissolved in the water (which <u>gives off</u> CO_2). The experiment can then be <u>repeated</u> with different temperatures of water or concentrations of sodium hydrogencarbonate.

You could also measure how much oxygen's produced by counting the bubbles — but it's not as accurate.

I'm working on sunshine — woah oh...*

Well, there's no denying these 'limiting factors' graphs are tricky. But you need to understand them, so get learning.

Q1   An experiment was carried out to find out the effect of temperature on the rate of photosynthesis.
Give two variables that should have been controlled in this experiment.   [2 marks]

As you may have noticed, photosynthesis makes me want to sing.

Revision Questions for Section 3a

Well, that's all for Section 3a — after that blast through everything photosynthesis, how about some questions.

- Try these questions and tick off each one when you get it right.
- When you've done all the questions for a topic and are completely happy with it, tick off the topic.

Photosynthesis (p.52-53) ☑

1) Where in a plant cell does photosynthesis take place?
2) What is the word summary for photosynthesis?
3) Which stage of photosynthesis requires light?
4) What molecule is split during the light reactions of photosynthesis?
5) True or False? Oxygen produced in the first stage of photosynthesis remains in the cell.
6) Which stage of photosynthesis involves a series of enzyme-controlled reactions?
7) Name the substance that provides energy for carbon fixation.
8) What substance is produced during carbon fixation?
9) Name the structural material that plants make from sugar.
10) Why is it beneficial for plants to convert some of the sugar they make into starch?
11) Other than making a structural material and starch, what else do plants use the sugar made in photosynthesis for?
12) Which chemical is used to test for the presence of starch in a leaf?

Rate of Photosynthesis (p.54-55) ☑

13) Why does the rate of photosynthesis affect the growth rate of a plant?
14) What is meant by a 'limiting factor' of photosynthesis?
15) If light and CO_2 are in plentiful supply, what factor must be limiting photosynthesis?
16) What effect would low light intensity have on plant growth?
17) What effect would a low carbon dioxide concentration have on the rate of photosynthesis?
18) What effect would a temperature above 45 °C usually have on the rate of photosynthesis? Why?
19) Describe an experiment you could use to investigate the effect of light intensity on the rate of photosynthesis.
20) How could you control the carbon dioxide concentration in an experiment to investigate the rate of photosynthesis?

Ecosystems and Competition

It's tough in the wild — there's always <u>competition</u> for <u>food</u> and other resources.

Ecosystems are Organised into Different Levels

Ecosystems have <u>different levels</u> of <u>organisation</u>:

1) <u>Individual</u> — **A** <u>single</u> organism.
2) <u>Population</u> — <u>All</u> the organisms of <u>one species</u> in a <u>habitat</u>. A <u>species</u> is a group of <u>similar</u> organisms that can <u>reproduce</u> with each other to give <u>fertile offspring</u>.
3) <u>Community</u> — **All** the organisms (<u>different species</u>) living in a habitat.
4) <u>Ecosystem</u> — A community of <u>organisms</u> along with all the <u>non-living</u> (<u>abiotic</u>) <u>conditions</u> (see next page).

> A habitat is the place where an organism lives, e.g. a rocky shore or a field.

The <u>variety</u> of life in an <u>ecosystem</u> is called <u>biodiversity</u> — the <u>greater</u> the variety in an ecosystem the <u>higher</u> its biodiversity. For example, there's a greater variety of species in a <u>tropical rainforest</u> than there is at the <u>north pole</u> — so the rainforest ecosystem has a <u>higher</u> biodiversity.

All Organisms in a Community Have a Niche

<u>All</u> organisms play a certain <u>role</u> within their <u>community</u> — this role is called a <u>niche</u>.
Every species has its own <u>unique</u> niche — a niche can only be occupied by <u>one</u> species.
The <u>factors</u> that determine an organism's niche are:

* The <u>resources</u> it needs from the ecosystem — e.g. light and nutrients.
* The <u>range of conditions</u> it can survive in — e.g. the temperature range a plant can grow in.
* The <u>interactions</u> it has with other organisms in the community. For example, this could be an interaction between a <u>predator</u> (an animal that feeds on other animals) and its <u>prey</u> (an animal that gets eaten by another animal). Or it could be an interaction where organisms <u>compete</u> for resources (see below).

Organisms Compete for Resources to Survive

1) Organisms need things from their <u>environment</u> and from <u>other organisms</u> to <u>survive</u> and <u>reproduce</u>. E.g.:
   * <u>Plants</u> need <u>light</u>, <u>space</u>, <u>water</u> and <u>nutrients</u> from the soil.
   * <u>Animals</u> need <u>space (territory)</u>, <u>shelter</u>, <u>food</u>, <u>water</u> and <u>mates</u>.
2) However, these <u>resources</u> are <u>limited</u> and many organisms within a community need the <u>same</u> resources. This means that when a resource is in <u>short supply</u>, organisms <u>compete</u> for those resources.
3) Sometimes organisms <u>compete</u> with organisms of <u>other species</u> — this is called <u>interspecific competition</u>.

> Red and grey <u>squirrels</u> live in the same habitat and eat the same food. <u>Competition</u> with the grey squirrels for these resources in some areas means there's <u>not enough food</u> for the <u>reds</u> — so the <u>population</u> of <u>red</u> squirrels is <u>decreasing</u>, while the population of grey squirrels is <u>increasing</u>.

4) Sometimes organisms <u>compete</u> with organisms of the <u>same species</u> — this is <u>intraspecific competition</u>.

> Trees of the <u>same</u> species growing next to each other will have to compete for <u>all the resources they need</u>. For example, the trees will compete to take up <u>water</u> and <u>nutrients</u> from the soil, and for <u>light</u> from the sun.

5) <u>Intraspecific</u> competition is more <u>intense</u> than <u>interspecific</u> competition. This is because the species that are competing occupy the same <u>niche</u> (see above) so they must <u>compete</u> for <u>everything</u>. In <u>interspecific</u> competition organisms only tend to compete for <u>one</u> or a <u>few</u> resources.

Intraspecific competition — fighting your brother for the last cake...

Interspecific competition is between <u>different</u> species like <u>inter</u>national competition is between <u>different</u> nations.

Q1 Describe what is meant by the term 'niche'.   **[1 mark]**

Abiotic and Biotic Factors

The environment in which organisms live <u>changes</u> all the time. The things that change are either
<u>abiotic</u> (non-living) or <u>biotic</u> (living) factors. These can have a big <u>effect</u> on a community...

Abiotic Factors Can Vary in an Ecosystem...

1) Abiotic factors are the <u>non-living</u> factors of an ecosystem that organisms interact with. They include:

- <u>Temperature</u>
- <u>pH</u>
- <u>Moisture level</u> (e.g. the amount of rainfall or moisture in the soil)
- <u>Light intensity</u>

2) Abiotic factors can affect <u>biodiversity</u> within an ecosystem (see previous page).
They can also affect the <u>distribution of organisms</u> (where they are found within a habitat). E.g.:

> There are relatively <u>few</u> species that can survive in <u>hot</u>, <u>dry</u> environments, so places with these
> abiotic factors have <u>low biodiversity</u>. The species that do live there need water to survive, so
> they're <u>more likely</u> to be found <u>near</u> water sources than in the <u>driest areas</u> of the <u>habitat</u>.

3) Any <u>change</u> to an abiotic factor can cause a <u>change</u> in <u>biodiversity</u> and the <u>distribution</u> of organisms. E.g.:

- A <u>decrease</u> in light intensity will reduce the rate at which plants <u>photosynthesise</u>. This could <u>reduce</u>
  the number of species that can <u>survive</u> in the ecosystem and cause a <u>decrease</u> in <u>biodiversity</u>.
- An <u>increase</u> in the <u>moisture level</u> of the soil in one area of a habitat
  could mean more plants of a particular <u>species</u> grow in that <u>area</u>.
  This would <u>alter</u> the <u>distribution</u> of that <u>species</u> in the habitat.

Organisms in an ecosystem depend on each other for survival (see p.62). So a change that affects one species often has knock-on effects for other species too.

...and So Can Biotic Factors

1) Biotic factors are the <u>living</u> factors of an ecosystem.

2) Just like with abiotic factors, biotic factors can <u>affect</u> the <u>biodiversity</u>
and the <u>distribution of organisms</u> within an ecosystem.

3) Here are some biotic factors you <u>need to know</u> and <u>examples</u> of how <u>changes</u> to them could affect species:

- <u>Predation</u> — if the <u>number of lions</u> (predators) in one part of a habitat <u>increases</u>
  then gazelles (prey) might move away from that area so they don't get eaten.
  This would affect the <u>distribution</u> of <u>gazelles</u> within the habitat.
- <u>Grazing</u> (a plant being eaten by an animal) — if the number of <u>rabbits</u> (grazers) in a
  habitat <u>decreases</u> then the number of plant species that can survive there might <u>increase</u>.
  This would <u>increase</u> the <u>biodiversity</u> of the ecosystem.
- <u>Competition</u> — if a new plant species in a field <u>out-competes</u> an existing plant species,
  it could mean that the existing plant species can <u>no longer survive</u> in <u>all areas</u> of the field.
  This would change its <u>distribution</u>.
- <u>Disease</u> — if a new <u>virus</u> (see p.45) appears in an ecosystem it could cause many
  organisms to die through <u>illness</u>, and could even wipe out <u>entire</u> populations.
  This would <u>reduce</u> the <u>biodiversity</u> of the ecosystem.
- <u>Availability of food</u> — if the <u>availability</u> of berries greatly increases then the ecosystem
  might be able to <u>support</u> a <u>greater</u> number of bird species that eat berries.
  This would <u>increase</u> the <u>biodiversity</u> of the ecosystem.

Revision — an abiotic factor causing stress in my community...

Humans can have a big impact on biodiversity and the distribution of organisms by disrupting the abiotic and
biotic factors of ecosystems. For example, air pollution can lead to acid rain — this can reduce the biodiversity of
ecosystems because many species cannot survive the low pH levels caused by acid rain.

Q1   Give two abiotic factors that could affect the community in an ecosystem.   [2 marks]

Investigating Ecosystems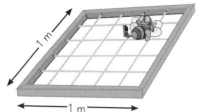

You'll be thrilled to know you can study the distribution of organisms. First up, using quadrats...

Use a Quadrat to Study The Distribution of Small Organisms

A quadrat is a square frame enclosing a known area, e.g. 1 m². To compare how common an organism is in two sample areas, just follow these simple steps:

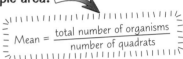
A quadrat

1) Place a 1 m² quadrat on the ground at a random point within the first sample area. E.g. divide the area into a grid and use a random number generator to pick coordinates. Otherwise, if all your samples are in one spot and everywhere else is different, the results you get won't be representative of the whole sample area. For more about random sampling take a look at page 75.

2) Count all the organisms you're interested in within the quadrat.

3) Repeat steps 1 and 2 lots of times. (The larger the sample size the better, see p.5.)

4) Work out the mean number of organisms per quadrat within the first sample area.

5) Repeat steps 1 to 4 in the second sample area.

6) Finally compare the two means. E.g. you might find 2 daisies per m² in the shade, and 22 daisies per m² (lots more) in an open field.

$$\text{Mean} = \frac{\text{total number of organisms}}{\text{number of quadrats}}$$

Estimate Population Sizes by Scaling Up from a Small Sample Area

To work out the population size of an organism in one sample area, you need to work out the mean number of organisms per m² (if your quadrat has an area of 1 m², this is the same as the mean number of organisms per quadrat, worked out above). Then just multiply the mean by the total area of the habitat:

EXAMPLE: Students used quadrats, each with an area of 0.25 m², to randomly sample daisies in a field. They found a mean of 10 daisies per quadrat. The field's area was 800 m². Estimate the population size of daisies in the field.

1) Work out the mean number of organisms per m². $1 \div 0.25 = 4$ $4 \times 10 = 40$ daisies per m²

2) Multiply the mean per m² by the total area (in m²) of the habitat. $= 40 \times 800$ $= 32\,000$ daisies in the field

Use Pitfall Traps to Investigate the Distribution of Small Animals

1) Pitfall traps are steep-sided containers that are sunk in a hole in the ground. The top is partly open.

2) Leave the trap overnight in your first sample area. Small animals (e.g. insects) that come along fall into the container and can't get out again, so you can count them.

3) Then set up a pitfall trap in your second sample area and compare what you find with the first sample area.

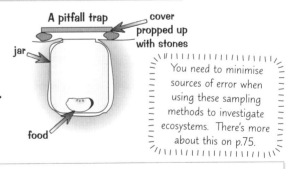
A pitfall trap — cover propped up with stones, jar, food

You need to minimise sources of error when using these sampling methods to investigate ecosystems. There's more about this on p.75.

Drat, drat and double drat — my favourite use of quadrats...

Choosing which sampling method to use often depends on the type of organism you're studying. E.g. quadrats are great for organisms that don't move such as plants, but traps are better for organisms that move around, like insects.

Q1 A student wants to investigate the distribution of buttercups in a field.
   a) Describe how the student could use quadrats to compare the number of buttercups in two different areas of the field. [3 marks]
   b) Suggest another sampling method the student could use if she was investigating the distribution of woodlice instead. [1 mark]

More on Investigating Ecosystems

Yep, there's still some more to learn about this stuff. Coming up we have <u>transects</u> and <u>keys</u> — lovely.

Use Transects to Study Distribution Along a Line   `PRACTICAL`

You can use lines called <u>transects</u> to help find out how organisms (like plants) are <u>distributed</u> across an area — e.g. if an organism becomes <u>more or less common</u> as you move from a hedge towards the middle of a field. Here's what to do:

1) <u>Mark out a line</u> in the area you want to study using a tape measure.

2) Then <u>collect data</u> along the line.

3) You can do this by just <u>counting</u> all the organisms you're interested in that <u>touch</u> the line.

4) Or, you can collect data by using <u>quadrats</u> (see previous page). These can be placed <u>next to</u> each other along the line or <u>at intervals</u>, for example, every 2 m.

tape measure

quadrat

Transects can be used in any ecosystem, not just fields. For example, along a beach.

5) Taking <u>measurements</u> of <u>abiotic factors</u> (see next page) at points along the transect can show how changes in these affect the distribution organisms in the habitat. E.g. in a coastal habitat, changes in <u>soil pH</u> and <u>soil depth</u> result in zones where different plants grow.

Keys are Used to Identify Organisms   `PRACTICAL`

1) A <u>key</u> is a <u>written tool</u> that you can use to figure out what an <u>unknown organism</u> is.

2) Keys are useful when carrying out sampling as they help you to <u>correctly identify</u> organisms you find.

3) You need to know about <u>paired-statement keys</u>. These keys have a series of <u>numbered pairs</u> of <u>statements</u>. For your mystery organism only <u>one</u> of the two statements will be <u>true</u>, e.g. wings present or wings absent.

4) Next to each of the statements is <u>a number</u> that tells you which pair of statements to <u>go to next</u>. You need to <u>follow</u> the <u>true</u> statement.

5) As you go through more and more pairs of statements you <u>narrow down your options further</u> until eventually you're just <u>left with one</u> possible species your organism could be. For example:

> <u>Part of a paired-statement key</u> is shown on the right. It can be used to identify <u>ladybird species</u>.
>
> 5. Black spots on wings   go to 6
>   No spots on wings   go to 11
> 6. Rings around wing spots   Eyed ladybird
>   No rings around wing spots   go to 9

6) You can even <u>construct</u> a paired-statement key yourself:

> 1) First you need a <u>sample</u> of <u>all</u> the organisms the key will <u>identify</u>.
>
> 2) <u>Split</u> your sample into <u>two groups</u> based on <u>one characteristic</u> and write down <u>two statements</u> that describe the groups (e.g. has 6 legs, has more than 6 legs).
>
> 3) Then split <u>each group</u> into <u>two</u> using a <u>different</u> characteristic, writing statements for each group.
>
> 4) Keep splitting your groups until you're left with only <u>pairs</u>. Then <u>link</u> your <u>statements</u> together in the <u>right order</u> and hey presto, you've made a key.

Identification keys — not much use in the world of home security...

Keys help you identify organisms you've found when sampling. This is pretty important when you want to talk about the different organisms that you've seen — it's not much use saying you found six slimy things in a pond...

Q1   Describe how a transect line and quadrats could be used to investigate the distribution of a species across a field.

[3 marks]

Investigating Factors Affecting Distribution

There's yet more fieldwork coming up folks. This page is all about inves... well, just read the page title.

You Need to Know How to Measure Abiotic Factors   PRACTICAL

1) As you saw on page 58, the distribution of organisms can be affected by abiotic factors. For example, in a playing field, you might find that daisies are more common in the open than under trees, because there's more light available in the open.

2) If you find there's a difference in the distribution of organisms in a habitat, you can investigate the factors that might be causing it.

3) For example, when looking into the distribution of daisies in the playing field mentioned above, you could measure light intensity both under the trees and in the open — finding a difference in light intensity could provide evidence for the idea that this is affecting the distribution of daisies.

4) Here's how you can measure the following abiotic factors:

- Use a thermometer to measure the temperature in different places.
- Use a soil moisture meter to measure the level of moisture in soil. To minimise sources of error and produce valid results, make sure the probe is inserted into the soil at the same depth each time and don't forget to wipe the probe between samples.
- Use a light meter to measure light intensity. Hold the meter at the level of the organisms you're investigating (ground level for daisies) and make sure it's at the same height and angle for every reading you take.
- Measure soil pH using indicator liquid — water is added to a soil sample and then an indicator liquid is added that changes colour depending on the pH. The colour is compared to a chart to find out the soil pH. Errors can be made when trying to match the colour exactly to the chart, so electronic pH meters can be used to get a more accurate pH value. As with the soil moisture meter, remember to insert the probe to the same depth every time and wipe between samples.

There's more on measuring temperature and pH on p.72-73.

Indicator Species Can Be Used to Assess Pollution   PRACTICAL

Pollution can affect the abiotic factors in an ecosystem (e.g. it can alter the concentration of gases in the air). Some organisms are very sensitive to changes in their environment and can be studied to assess the quality of the environment, such as the level of pollution — these organisms are known as indicator species.

- Some animals, like stonefly larvae and freshwater shrimps are good indicators for water pollution because they're very sensitive to the concentration of dissolved oxygen in the water — if you find stonefly larvae in a river, it indicates that the water is clean.
- Other animals have adapted to live in polluted conditions — so if you see a lot of them you know there's a problem. E.g. blood worms and sludge worms indicate highly polluted water.

Polluted water can lead to reduced oxygen availability in the water (see p.65).

- Air pollution can be monitored by looking at particular types of lichen that are very sensitive to the concentration of sulfur dioxide in the atmosphere. (Sulfur dioxide is a pollutant released from car exhausts, power stations, etc.) E.g. the air is clean if there are lots of lichen — especially bushy lichen, which need cleaner air than crusty lichen.

There are a couple of ways of using indicator species to assess the level of pollution, for example:

1) You could do a simple survey to see if an indicator species is present or absent from an area. This is a quick way of telling whether an area is polluted or not, but it's no good for telling how polluted an area is.

2) You could investigate the distribution of an indicator species in a habitat. The numbers of the indicator species found in different areas will allow you to assess how pollution levels vary throughout the habitat.

Teenagers are an indicator species — not found in clean rooms...

Make sure you know how to measure abiotic factors and have got your head around those fussy indicator species.

Q1   Name a piece of equipment that can be used to measure light intensity.   [1 mark]

Food Chains and Food Webs

If you like <u>food</u>, and you like <u>chains</u>, then <u>food chains</u> might just blow your mind. Strap yourself
in and prepare for some 'edge of your seat' learning, because the show is about to begin...

Food Chains Show What's Eaten by What in an Ecosystem

1) <u>Food chains</u> always start with a <u>producer</u>.
   Producers <u>make</u> (produce) <u>their own food</u> using <u>energy</u> from the sun.

2) Producers are usually <u>green plants</u> — they make <u>sugar</u> by <u>photosynthesis</u> (see p.52).

3) When a green plant produces sugar, some of it is used to make <u>other biological molecules</u> in the plant.
   This <u>stores</u> some of the <u>energy</u> from the sun in the <u>living material</u> of the plant.

4) <u>Energy</u> is <u>transferred</u> through living organisms in an ecosystem when organisms <u>eat</u> other organisms.

5) An organism that eats another organism is called a <u>consumer</u>. A consumer
   can be a <u>herbivore</u> (one that only eats plants), a <u>carnivore</u> (one that only eats
   animals) or an <u>omnivore</u> (one that eats both plants and animals).

6) Each stage in a food chain is called a <u>trophic level</u>. <u>Producers</u> are the <u>first</u> trophic level.

7) Here's an <u>example</u> of a food chain:

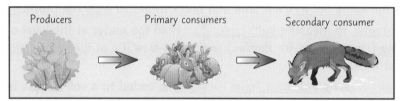

The arrows in a
food chain show
you the direction
of energy transfer.

Food Webs Show How Food Chains are Linked

1) There are <u>many different species</u> within an ecosystem — which means <u>lots of
   different</u> possible <u>food chains</u>. You can draw a <u>food web</u> to show them.

2) All the species in a food web <u>depend</u> on each other for survival.

3) This means that a change in the size of <u>one population</u> will <u>affect</u>
   the sizes of <u>other populations</u> in the ecosystem.

In the food web on the right, if lots of
<u>water spiders died</u>, then:

- There would be <u>less food</u> for the <u>frogs</u>,
  so their numbers might <u>decrease</u>.
- The number of <u>mayfly larvae</u>
  might <u>increase</u> since the water
  spiders wouldn't be eating them.
- The <u>diving beetles</u> wouldn't be
  <u>competing</u> with the water spiders for
  food, so their numbers might <u>increase</u>.

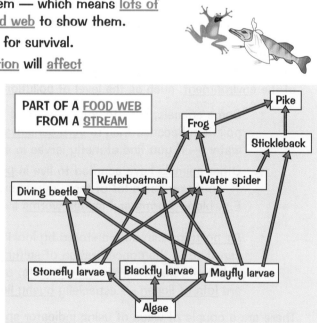

PART OF A <u>FOOD WEB</u>
FROM A <u>STREAM</u>

Food webs — nothing to do with ordering pizza online, I'm afraid...

Food webs are handy for looking at relationships between individual species. Unfortunately you hardly ever see
simple food webs in the real world — they're normally as tangled together and interlinked as a bowl of spaghetti.

Q1   The diagram on the right shows part of a food web.
      Using the diagram, suggest what might happen to the
      population size of ladybirds if the population of mice increased.

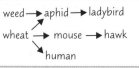

[2 marks]

Energy in Ecosystems

This page might not be the most interesting page, but at least you're not getting <u>eaten</u> by a <u>load</u> of <u>rabbits</u>...

Energy is Lost Between each Trophic Level

1) As you saw on the previous page, <u>energy</u> is <u>transferred</u> through the living organisms of an ecosystem. However, the <u>majority</u> of energy is <u>lost</u> and is <u>not transferred</u> from one <u>trophic level</u> to the <u>next</u>.

2) Lots of energy is <u>lost</u> from food chains because animals need to <u>use energy</u> for <u>movement</u> and for <u>keeping warm</u> (so energy is lost as <u>heat</u>).

3) Energy is also lost because <u>not all parts</u> of organisms that are eaten can be digested — <u>undigested material</u> (and the energy it contains) is lost in <u>faeces</u>.

4) So only a <u>small</u> amount of the energy an organism takes in when it eats is actually used for <u>growth</u> (for building more biological material that <u>stores</u> energy).

5) This explains why you hardly ever get <u>food chains</u> with more than about <u>five trophic levels</u>. So much energy is lost at each stage that there's not enough left to support more organisms after four or five stages. You also tend to get <u>fewer organisms</u> at each trophic level (although this <u>isn't always</u> the case, see below).

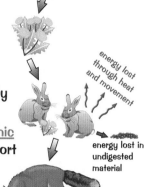

energy lost through heat and movement

energy lost in undigested material

You Need to Understand Pyramids of Energy...

A <u>pyramid of energy</u> is a <u>model</u> that represents the <u>transfer of energy</u> in a food chain. Here's a pyramid of energy for the food chain, 'rosebush → caterpillar → bird'.

1) Each <u>bar</u> on a pyramid of energy shows the <u>amount of energy</u> stored at that stage of the food chain.

| Bird |
| Caterpillars |
| Rosebush |

2) Pyramids of energy are always <u>shaped</u> like a <u>true pyramid</u> (i.e. the bars get progressively smaller from the bottom to the top). That's because <u>energy is lost</u> at each stage in the food chain.

3) So the 'rosebush' bar here is <u>longer</u> than the 'caterpillars' bar, which in turn is <u>longer</u> than the 'bird' bar.

4) The <u>rosebush</u> goes at the <u>bottom</u> because it's at the start of the food chain — it's the producer.

...and Pyramids of Numbers

A <u>pyramid of numbers</u> is a <u>model</u> that represents the <u>number of organisms</u> at <u>each stage</u> in a food chain. Here's a pyramid of numbers for the <u>same</u> food chain as the pyramid of energy above.

1) Each <u>bar</u> on a pyramid of numbers shows the <u>number of organisms</u> at that stage of the food chain.

1 bird
20 caterpillars
1 rosebush

2) Many pyramids of numbers are shaped like a <u>true pyramid</u> because organisms in one trophic level have to eat <u>a lot</u> of organisms from the level below to survive.

3) However, sometimes pyramids of numbers are <u>not</u> shaped like true pyramids. This happens when an organism in a food chain is <u>much bigger</u> than the organism that <u>eats</u> it. E.g. a <u>rosebush</u> is much bigger than a <u>caterpillar</u>. This means that <u>many</u> caterpillars can feed on just <u>one</u> rosebush, so the bars in the pyramid of numbers <u>do not</u> get progressively smaller.

Pyramids are a piece of cake — just ask the Egyptians...

Pyramids of numbers could also have a big bar across the top if, for example, there were loads of fleas feeding on one fox. But there would be less energy in all the fleas than the fox, so the energy pyramid would look normal.

Q1 Look at the two diagrams on the right. One is a pyramid of energy and one is a pyramid of numbers. Which one is the pyramid of numbers? Explain your answer.

A   B

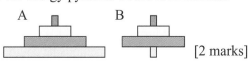

[2 marks]

Increasing Crop Yields — Pesticides

We have a bit more <u>control</u> over our <u>food chains</u> than other organisms because we <u>farm</u> most of our <u>food</u>. But making sure there's enough <u>energy</u> in the food chains to keep us all going is <u>no easy job</u>.

We Need to Increase Crop Yields to Feed the Future Population

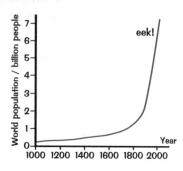

1) The world's <u>population</u> is <u>rising very quickly</u>, and it's not slowing down — look at the graph...

2) As the <u>population</u> continues to <u>grow</u>, we need to <u>produce more food</u> so that each person still has the <u>same amount</u> of food to eat.

3) We can't keep using more and more <u>land</u> for farming, so we need to <u>increase crop yields</u> (the amount of crops that are grown per area of land).

4) Two ways farmers are increasing crop yields is by using <u>fertilisers</u> to make plants <u>grow better</u> (see next page) and by using <u>pesticides</u> to <u>kill</u> pests (organisms that <u>destroy</u> plants or <u>slow</u> their growth) — see below.

Pesticides Can Kill Both Plant and Animal Pests

1) <u>Pesticides</u> are a form of <u>chemical pest control</u> which are sprayed onto crops to <u>kill</u> the pests that <u>damage</u> them. They're often <u>poisonous</u> to <u>humans</u>, so they must be used carefully to keep the amount of pesticide in <u>food</u> below a <u>safe level</u>.

2) There are <u>different types</u> of pesticide which target different types of pest. For example, <u>insecticides</u> kill insects and <u>herbicides</u> kill unwanted plants (e.g. weeds).

3) Pesticides can cause <u>problems</u>. For example, some pesticides also <u>harm other wildlife</u> that aren't pests, like bees and ladybirds. This can cause a <u>shortage of food</u> for animals higher up the food chain.

4) Also some pesticides <u>accumulate</u> (build up) over time in organisms that <u>eat plants</u> which have been <u>sprayed</u> with pesticides. The pesticides then get <u>passed along</u> the food chain when these animals are eaten. At each stage of the food chain, the <u>concentration</u> of the pesticide <u>increases</u>, meaning its <u>toxicity increases</u> — so organisms at the top of the chain can receive a <u>lethal</u> (deadly) dose of the pesticide. When toxic substances <u>build up</u> in organisms like this it's called <u>bioaccumulation</u>.

Biological Control is an Alternative to Using Pesticides

1) <u>Biological control</u> involves using <u>other organisms</u> to reduce the numbers of pests. This is done by <u>encouraging wild organisms</u> or <u>adding new ones</u>.

2) The helpful organisms could be <u>predators</u> (e.g. ladybirds eat aphids), or <u>disease-causing</u> organisms (e.g. bacteria that affect caterpillars).

3) Biological control can have a <u>longer-lasting</u> effect than spraying pesticides, and be <u>less harmful</u> to <u>wildlife</u>. But introducing new organisms can cause <u>problems</u> — e.g. <u>cane toads</u> were introduced to Australia to eat beetles, but they're now a major <u>pest</u> themselves because they poison the native species that eat them.

4) Biological control can be considered a <u>safer alternative</u> to pesticides. This is because <u>no chemicals are used</u>, so there's <u>less pollution</u>, a lower <u>risk to people</u> eating the food and <u>no passing of chemicals along food chains</u>.

"Oi aphids — you'd better stay outta my field or you'll regret it..."

The world's population is growing by around 80 million people each year. We'll need to greatly increase global food yields to keep everyone fed.

Year	1	2	3	4
Yield of potatoes (tonnes per hectare)	30	28	32	34

Q1   The table shows the yield of potatoes that a farmer has produced during the last four years.

     a)   Calculate the mean yield across all the years shown.   [1 mark]

     b)   The farmer increased his potato yield by controlling a beetle pest that eats potato plants. Describe two methods he could have used to control the beetle.   [2 marks]

Increasing Crop Yields — Fertilisers

Fertilisers are really helpful for <u>increasing crop yields</u> — but they can also have <u>negative impacts</u> on <u>ecosystems</u>.

Fertilisers Are Used to Ensure Crops Have Enough Nitrates

1) Plants need to take in certain <u>chemicals</u> from the <u>soil</u> in order to <u>grow</u> properly. <u>Nitrates</u> are really important chemicals they need.

2) Plants take up <u>nitrates</u> that are <u>dissolved</u> in <u>water</u> in the <u>soil</u>.

3) They need nitrates to make <u>amino acids</u>, which are used for <u>protein synthesis</u> (see p.23).

4) The <u>amino acids</u> made by plants are <u>passed to animals</u> that eat the plants, and then they're passed to <u>other animals</u> further up the food chain. Just like plants, animals also need amino acids for <u>protein synthesis</u>.

5) Being able to make proteins is essential for <u>plant growth</u>, so it's important that there are plenty of nitrates in the <u>soil</u>.

6) Farmers try to <u>boost</u> the level of nitrates in the soil by <u>adding</u> fertilisers that contain nitrates. This helps to <u>maximise</u> plant growth and therefore <u>increases</u> crop yields.

Animals can't make all of the amino acids they need themselves, so it's really important that plants are able to make them.

Fertilisers also contain other chemicals that plants need to grow properly, e.g. phosphate and potassium.

Fertilisers Can Leach into Fresh Water

You might think <u>fertilisers</u> would be a good thing for the environment because they make plants grow faster. But they cause <u>big problems</u> when they end up in freshwater sources, such as <u>rivers</u> and <u>lakes</u> — here's how:

1) If <u>too much fertiliser</u> is applied and it <u>rains</u> afterwards, nitrates are easily <u>leached</u> (washed through the soil) into rivers and lakes.

2) This can cause serious <u>damage</u> to river and lake <u>ecosystems</u>:

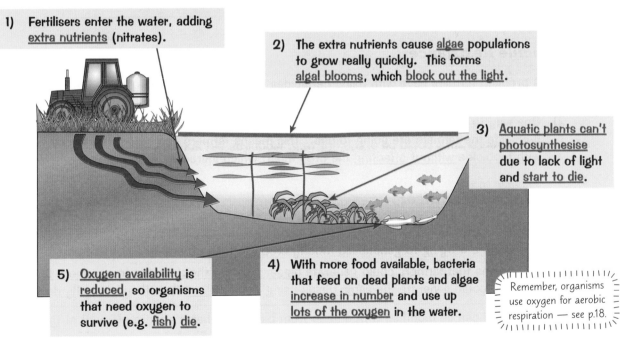

1) Fertilisers enter the water, adding <u>extra nutrients</u> (nitrates).

2) The extra nutrients cause <u>algae</u> populations to grow really quickly. This forms <u>algal blooms</u>, which <u>block out the light</u>.

3) <u>Aquatic plants can't photosynthesise</u> due to lack of light and <u>start to die</u>.

4) With more food available, bacteria that feed on dead plants and algae <u>increase in number</u> and use up <u>lots of the oxygen</u> in the water.

5) <u>Oxygen availability</u> is <u>reduced</u>, so organisms that need oxygen to survive (e.g. <u>fish</u>) <u>die</u>.

Remember, organisms use oxygen for aerobic respiration — see p.18.

Don't get wet in the rain, these facts could leach out of your head...

We're using more fertilisers now than ever — while we need fertilisers to keep increasing yields, increased usage also means it's more likely to cause environmental problems. Finding an alternative to chemical fertilisers is a big challenge — see the next page for one way that we might be able to stop using so many fertilisers.

Q1   a) How do plants obtain nitrates?   [1 mark]

      b) Describe how nitrates are used in plants.   [2 marks]

Increasing Crop Yields — GM Crops

Fertilisers and pest control aren't the only options for increasing yields. Oh no, there's one more that you need to know about. I know you can't wait to read about it so I won't waffle on any longer...

Crop Plants can be Genetically Modified to Increase Yields

1) Genetic engineering can be used to transfer useful genes into crop plants. This means they'll develop the useful characteristics coded for by the inserted gene.

2) Genetically modified (GM) crops are crop plants that have had their genes altered by genetic engineering.

3) GM crops can increase food production in many different ways...

There's more on genetic engineering on page 26.

Insect Resistance

Crops can be genetically modified to make them resistant to insect pests — this prevents them from being eaten or damaged and so increases crop yield.

1) There's a bacterium called *Bacillus thuringiensis* (Bt) which produces a toxin (poison) that kills many of the insect larvae that are harmful to crops.

2) The gene for the Bt toxin is inserted into crops, like corn, cotton and tomatoes, which then produce the toxin in their stems and leaves — making them resistant to the insect pests.

3) The toxin is specific to insect pests — it's harmless to humans, animals and other insects.

4) A good thing about Bt crops is that farmers need to apply less pesticide (because the crops already have it built into them). This avoids the negative impacts of pesticide use (see p.64).

5) There's a drawback to Bt crops though. There's a danger that insects might develop resistance to the toxin and no longer be killed by it.

Herbicide Resistance

1) A problem farmers have with using herbicides is that it can be tricky to kill the unwanted plants (the weeds) without harming the crop plants.

2) One way to do this is to genetically modify the crop plants to be resistant to the herbicide the farmers are going to use. This means farmers can spray their crops with herbicide without affecting the crop itself, which increases crop yields.

Require Less Fertiliser

1) Fertilisers are expensive and can cause environmental problems (see previous page).

2) Scientists are trying to genetically modify crops to take up and use nutrients more efficiently.

3) This means that farmers could generate bigger yields without having to use more fertiliser. (Or they could generate the same yields using less fertiliser than they currently do.)

1) Rice can be modified with a gene from barley so that it's more efficient at taking up nitrates from the soil (see previous page).

2) This means that farmers don't need to add extra fertilisers to the soil to achieve bigger yields, because the GM rice is able to take up more nitrates from the current amount of fertiliser.

I fancy getting insect resistance — it'd really improve picnics...

Make sure you can explain how genetically modifying crops can reduce the use of both pesticides and fertilisers.

Q1   Give three ways in which crop plants can be genetically modified to increase yield.   [3 marks]

Revision Questions for Section 3b

It's time to say goodbye to Section 3b — but not before a healthy dose of questions to test yourself with...
- Try these questions and tick off each one when you get it right.
- When you've done all the questions for a topic and are completely happy with it, tick off the topic.

Ecosystems and Competition (p.57-58) ☑

1) Define 'community'. ☑
2) What is meant by biodiversity in an ecosystem? ☑
3) Give three factors that determine an organism's niche. ☑
4) What is meant by the term: a) predator, b) prey? ☑
5) Why do organisms compete with each other? ☑
6) Give three resources that plants compete for in an ecosystem. ☑
7) Give three resources that animals compete for in an ecosystem. ☑
8) What is intraspecific competition? ☑
9) Which type of competition (intraspecific or interspecific) is more intense? Explain why. ☑
10) True or false? A change in the abiotic factors of an ecosystem can effect biodiversity. ☑
11) Explain how a change in predation could affect the distribution of a species. ☑
12) Other than predation, give three biotic factors that could affect the community in an ecosystem. ☑

Investigating Ecosystems (p.59-61) ☑

13) What is a quadrat? ☑
14) Briefly describe how you could use quadrats to estimate the population size of a species. ☑
15) What is a paired-statement key? ☑
16) Describe how you could measure the pH of soil. ☑
17) What is an indicator species and why might you investigate the distribution of one? ☑

Food Chains, Food Webs and Energy in Ecosystems (p.62-63) ☐

18) What is shown in food chains? ☑
19) Would you find a producer at the start or end of a food chain? ☑
20) What is a consumer? ☑
21) What is: a) a herbivore, b) a carnivore, c) an omnivore? ☑
22) Give three ways that energy is lost from a food chain. ☑
23) True or false? Pyramids of energy are always pyramid-shaped. ☑
24) What does each bar on a pyramid of energy represent? ☑
25) What is meant by the term 'pyramid of numbers'? ☑

Increasing Crop Yields (p64-66) ☐

26) Why is it becoming more and more important for us to increase crop yields? ☑
27) Describe how using pesticides can increase crop yields. ☑
28) Describe how the bioaccumulation of pesticides occurs. ☑
29) How do animals obtain amino acids? ☑
30) Explain how the leaching of fertilisers into fresh water can cause the death of organisms. ☑
31) How can genetic engineering be used to reduce the use of fertilisers? ☐

Mutations

Evolution is the <u>slow and continuous change</u> of organisms from one generation to the next. Evolution can't happen without <u>genetic variation</u> — that's where evolution's best friends, <u>mutations</u>, come in...

Mutations are Changes to the Genetic Code

1) <u>Occasionally</u> a gene may <u>mutate</u>. A mutation is a <u>rare</u>, <u>random change</u> in an organism's <u>genetic material</u> that can be <u>inherited</u>.

2) Mutations <u>change the sequence</u> of <u>DNA bases</u> in a gene, which produces a <u>new allele</u> (a different form of the gene). Mutations are the <u>only source</u> of new alleles.

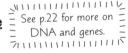
See p.22 for more on DNA and genes.

3) As the <u>sequence</u> of DNA bases <u>codes</u> for the sequence of <u>amino acids</u> that make up a <u>protein</u> (see page 23), mutations to a gene <u>sometimes</u> lead to <u>changes</u> in the protein that it codes for.

> <u>Enzymes</u> are proteins which need an active site with a <u>very specific shape</u> to be able to work properly (see p.24). A mutation in the gene that codes for an enzyme could lead to a <u>change in the shape</u> of an enzyme's active site — altering its function. A mutation could also <u>stop the production</u> of the enzyme altogether.

Well, I s'pose it's time for some new jeans.

Mutations Can Lead to a Different Phenotype

1) Some mutations have <u>bigger effects</u> on an organism's <u>phenotype</u> than others:

Remember, an organism's phenotype is the characteristics that it displays (see p.32).

- <u>Most</u> mutations have <u>no effect</u> on the phenotype — they're <u>neutral</u>. For example, if the mutation occurs in an unimportant region of the DNA, or if a mutation still codes for the same amino acid, the protein's <u>structure</u> and <u>function</u> will be <u>unaffected</u>. A mutation will also usually have no effect if it occurs in a <u>recessive</u> allele.

See p.33 for more on recessive alleles.

- <u>Some</u> mutations have a <u>small effect</u> on the phenotype. This happens when the change in amino acid only has a <u>slight effect</u> on the protein's structure and function — so the individual's characteristics are only altered <u>very slightly</u>.

- Very <u>rarely</u>, a mutation will have a <u>significant effect</u> on phenotype. For example, it might result in a <u>very different</u> protein which can <u>no longer</u> carry out its function.

2) Mutations that affect an organism's <u>phenotype</u> can have an <u>effect</u> on the organism's chance of <u>survival</u>. The mutation could be a survival <u>advantage</u> or <u>disadvantage</u>. For example:

> 1) A mutation that led to a deer having <u>bright orange</u> fur would be likely to <u>reduce</u> its chance of <u>survival</u> because it might be spotted <u>more easily</u> by <u>predators</u>.
>
> 2) A mutation that led to a deer being able to run <u>quicker</u> might <u>increase</u> its chance of <u>survival</u> because it could <u>escape</u> more easily <u>from predators</u>.

Environmental Factors Can Increase the Rate of Mutation

1) Mutations happen <u>spontaneously</u> — when a chromosome doesn't quite copy itself properly, e.g. during mitosis (see p.28).

2) However, the chance of mutation is <u>increased</u> by being exposed to <u>ionising radiation</u> (e.g. X-rays, gamma rays or ultraviolet rays) or <u>chemicals</u> called <u>mutagens</u> (e.g. chemicals in tobacco).

3) These environmental factors are <u>dangerous</u> because they <u>increase</u> the <u>rate of mutation</u>, which <u>increases</u> the chance of <u>harmful mutations</u>.

Some mutations can lead to uncontrolled cell growth and division, which can lead to cancer.

Some mutations make you find revising enjoyable...

Mutations might sound alarming, but actually most are tiny changes that don't affect phenotype at all.

Q1   State the meaning of the term 'neutral mutation'.   [1 mark]

Natural Selection

Natural selection is a process by which species evolve. It basically means that the above-average organisms in a species are more likely to survive and reproduce than the more rubbishy ones. And so, eventually, the traits that make organisms above-average become more common. Don't write it like that in your exam though...

Natural Selection Increases Advantageous Phenotypes

1) As you saw on the previous page, new alleles arise when DNA randomly mutates and occasionally the new alleles have an effect on an organism's phenotype.

2) New alleles that do affect phenotype can give rise to characteristics that make an organism better adapted (suited) to its environment and its niche (the role it plays in a ecosystem — see p.57). This means that the organisms that inherit these favourable alleles will have an advantageous phenotype.

3) Populations produce more offspring than the ecosystem can support. This means not all the organisms in a population can survive and reproduce. Selection pressures (environmental factors such as predation, disease and competition) affect which organisms are able to survive and reproduce.

4) Individuals with alleles that give advantageous phenotypes will have a better chance of overcoming the selection pressures, and have an increased chance of surviving, reproducing and passing on their genes.

5) A greater proportion of individuals in the next generation will inherit the favourable alleles so they'll also have the selective advantages (the phenotypes that help survival under the selection pressures).

6) Over many generations, the favourable alleles occur more frequently in the population. The 'best' characteristics are naturally selected and more and more of the population has the adaptation (an adaptation is an inherited characteristic that makes an organism more likely to survive in its environment or niche).

7) Natural selection, (also called 'survival of the fittest') only occurs when there are selection pressures acting on a species. Here's an example:

Once upon a time maybe all rabbits had short ears and managed OK. Then one day a mutated gene meant that one rabbit popped out with big ears. This rabbit could hear better and was always the first to dive for cover at the sound of a predator. Pretty soon he's fathered a whole family of rabbits with big ears, all diving for cover before the other rabbits, and before you know it, there are only big-eared rabbits left — because the rest just didn't hear trouble coming quick enough.

FOX!

Predation is the selection pressure in this example.

Populations can Evolve in Response to Changes in their Environment

1) Populations of species may show a lot of genetic variation — this means that there's a mix of alleles for different characteristics present in the population.

2) This variation allows populations to evolve over time, through natural selection, in response to changes in their environment, e.g. the climate becoming warmer.

3) This is because some organisms may have characteristics that make them better suited to the changing conditions, e.g. a thinner coat.

4) Organisms that are better suited to their environment will be more likely to survive, reproduce and pass on their useful alleles to their offspring, meaning the useful characteristic becomes more common over time, and the species evolves.

Ah, lovely.

'Natural selection' — sounds like vegan chocolates...

In terms of evolution, it's no good an organism being great at surviving if it doesn't breed and pass on its genes. And it'll only be good at surviving if it inherits great alleles or has awesome mutations in its DNA.

Q1   Musk oxen have thick fur, which is advantageous in the cold climate in which they live. Explain how the musk oxen may have developed this characteristic over many years.   [4 marks]

Speciation

Evolution by natural selection can lead to the development of different species — this is called speciation.

Isolation and Natural selection can Lead to Speciation

1) Speciation occurs when populations of the same species become so different that they can no longer successfully interbreed to produce fertile offspring.

2) This can happen when parts of a population are isolated (separated) from each other. The different sub-populations will occupy different niches, so the selection pressures acting on them will be different.

3) Mutations will cause new alleles to arise in each group. Different alleles will become more common in each sub-population due to natural selection operating differently on the groups (see previous page).

4) Eventually, individuals from the sub-populations will be so genetically different that they won't be able to breed with one another to produce fertile offspring. The two groups will have become separate species.

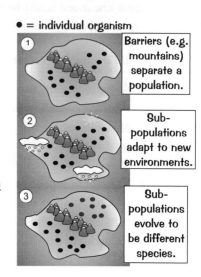

• = individual organism

Barriers (e.g. mountains) separate a population.

Sub-populations adapt to new environments.

Sub-populations evolve to be different species.

There are Different Reasons Why a Population can Separate

The factor that causes parts of a population to become isolated is called an isolation barrier. An isolation barrier can be geographical, ecological or behavioural:

GEOGRAPHICAL

Geographical features like rivers, mountains and seas can separate a population.

St Kilda is a small group of islands in the Outer Hebrides. Many years ago, it's thought that part of the wren population from mainland Scotland managed to fly to St. Kilda (probably helped by strong winds). The wren population survived and has gradually adapted to its niche — it's now bigger and different in colour to mainland wrens but it's not yet classed as a separate species. The St Kilda wren is isolated from the mainland wren by the sea. Members of the two populations could possibly fly to each other, but the long distance and rough conditions make this unlikely.

ECOLOGICAL

A population may become separated if parts of the population occupy different ecological niches. E.g. part of a population may start to occupy a different habitat within the same ecosystem, or may live in an area with different levels of abiotic factors, such as pH or salinity (salt concentration). The sub-populations will become isolated as they adapt to their different ecological niches.

See p.58 for more on abiotic factors.

Millions of years ago, it's likely that all African elephants lived in forest habitats and were all part of the same species. However, climate change created more savannah (grassy plains) and part of the African elephant population adapted to live in this new habitat, while the other part remained living in forests. Gradually, speciation occurred, so now there are two species of African elephant — African savannah elephants and African forest elephants.

BEHAVIOURAL

A population can become separated by differences in behaviour. Different behaviour displayed by members of a sub-population can mean they're less likely to breed with the rest of the population.

Hawthorn flies are attracted to the scent of hawthorn fruit, so this is where they mate and lay their eggs. However, around 200 years ago a sub-population of hawthorn flies began laying their eggs on apples rather than hawthorn fruit. Gradually, the population size of these 'apple flies' is growing and it's thought that the behavioural differences (where they choose to lay their eggs) may eventually lead to them becoming a separate species from hawthorn flies.

Not revising is a barrier that'll isolate you from good marks...

Well isn't speciation riveting... Put some time into learning this page, then maybe grab a biscuit.

Q1 Give three examples of ecological isolation barriers. [3 marks]

Revision Questions for Section 3c

Be sure to do all the questions because trust me, they'll give you an advantage on all things <u>Section 3c</u>.

- Try these questions and <u>tick off each one</u> when you <u>get it right</u>.
- When you've done <u>all the questions</u> for a topic and are <u>completely happy</u> with it, tick off the topic.

Mutations (p.68) ☑

1) What is a mutation?
2) True or False? Mutations are the only source of new alleles.
3) Why do some mutations have no effect on phenotype?
4) Explain how a mutation can affect the survival of an organism.
5) True or False? Mutations occur spontaneously.
6) Give two environmental factors that can increase the rate of mutation.

Natural Selection (p.69) ☐

7) Explain how a mutation may make an organism better adapted to its niche.
8) What is meant by the term 'selection pressure'?
9) What is an 'adaptation'?
10) Give another name for natural selection.
11) How does genetic variation help a species evolve in response to a change in the environment?

Speciation (p.70) ☐

12) What is speciation?
13) Why do different alleles become common in isolated populations?
14) Other than behavioural isolation, name two types of isolation barrier.
15) Describe how behavioural isolation can lead to speciation.

PRACTICAL   **Apparatus and Techniques**

Your experimental knowledge could be tested in the exam. This book covers loads of the practical apparatus and techniques you might need to know about — this section just covers some extra bits and bobs...

You Should Know What Different Apparatus is Used For and How to Use It

1) Using Vessels

1) Vessels, like beakers, test tubes and boiling tubes, are used to hold substances (usually to either mix or heat them) and are used across many common experiments.

2) Vessels are made of glass, so you need to make sure you're using them safely (see p.74). Boiling tubes are bigger than test tubes and are made of thicker glass — they're designed for heating substances to high temperatures (test tubes are not suitable for this).

3) Other pieces of equipment like tongs and funnels are useful when working with vessels. Tongs are used to pick up hot vessels, and funnels help you to not spill when pouring liquid into a vessel.

2) Measuring Time

1) If your experiment involves timing something (e.g. how long a reaction takes to happen) or taking measurements at regular intervals, it's probably best to use a stopwatch.

2) Using a stopwatch that measures to the nearest 0.1 s will make your results more accurate.

3) Always make sure you start and stop the stopwatch at exactly the right time. For example, if you're investigating the rate of a reaction, you should start timing at the exact moment you mix the reagents and start the reaction.

4) It's a good idea to get the same person to do the timing so the results are as precise as possible.

3) Measuring Temperature

You can use a thermometer to measure temperature. Make sure that the bulb of the thermometer is completely submerged in the substance you're measuring and that you wait for the temperature to stabilise before you take your initial reading. Read off the scale on the thermometer at eye level to make sure your reading is correct.

When you're reading off a scale, write down the value of the graduation that the amount is closest to. If it's exactly halfway between two values, round up.

4) Measuring the Volume of a Liquid

There's more than one way to measure the volume of a liquid. Whichever method you use, always read the volume from the bottom of the meniscus (the curved upper surface of the liquid) when it's at eye level.

Read volume from here — the bottom of the meniscus.

- Using a pipette — Pipettes are used to suck up and transfer volumes of liquid between containers. Dropping pipettes are used to transfer drops of liquid. Graduated pipettes are used to transfer accurate volumes. A pipette filler is attached to the end of a graduated pipette, to control the amount of liquid being drawn up.

- Using a measuring cylinder — Measuring cylinders come in all different sizes. Make sure you choose one that's the right size for the measurement you want to make. It's no good using a huge 1 dm³ cylinder to measure out 2 cm³ of a liquid — the graduations will be too big, and you'll end up with massive errors. It'd be much better to use one that measures up to 10 cm³.

5) Measuring the Volume of a Gas

1) To accurately measure the volume of gas, you should use a gas syringe.

2) Alternatively, you can use an upturned measuring cylinder filled with water. The gas will displace the water so you can read the volume off the scale.

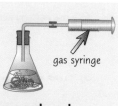

gas syringe

3) Other methods to measure the amount of gas include counting the bubbles produced or measuring the length of a gas bubble drawn along a tube (see p.55). These methods are less accurate because they don't tell you the total volume of gas produced. However, they will give you relative amounts of gas to compare results.

4) When you're measuring a gas, you need to make sure that the equipment is set up so that none of the gas can escape, otherwise your results won't be accurate.

Apparatus and Techniques PRACTICAL

6) Measuring Mass

To weigh a substance, start by putting the <u>container</u> you are weighing your substance into on a <u>balance</u>. Set the balance to exactly <u>zero</u> and then weigh out the correct amount of your substance. Easy peasy.

7) Measuring pH

The method you should use to measure pH depends on what your experiment is.

1) <u>Indicators</u> are dyes that <u>change colour</u> depending on whether they're in an <u>acid</u> or an <u>alkali</u>. You use them by adding a couple of drops of the indicator to the solution you're interested in. <u>Universal indicator</u> is a <u>mixture</u> of indicators that changes colour <u>gradually</u> as pH changes. It's useful for <u>estimating</u> the pH of a solution based on its colour.

2) <u>Indicator paper</u> is useful if you don't want to colour the entire solution that you're testing. It <u>changes colour</u> depending on the pH of the solution it touches. You can also hold a piece of <u>damp indicator paper</u> in a <u>gas sample</u> to test its pH.

Blue litmus paper turns <u>red</u> in acidic conditions and red litmus paper turns <u>blue</u> in alkaline conditions.

3) <u>pH meters</u> have a <u>digital display</u> that gives an <u>accurate value</u> for the pH of a solution.

You Can Grow Bacteria in the Lab

1) Bacteria (and some other microorganisms) are <u>cultured</u> (grown) in a <u>growth medium</u>, which contains the <u>carbohydrates</u>, <u>minerals</u>, <u>proteins</u> and <u>vitamins</u> they need to grow.

2) The growth medium used can be a <u>nutrient broth solution</u> or solid <u>agar jelly</u>.

3) Bacteria grown on agar 'plates' will form visible <u>colonies</u> on the <u>surface</u> of the jelly, or will <u>spread out</u> to give an even covering.

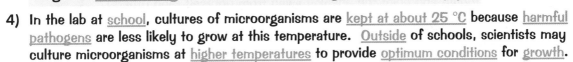

inoculating loop

Petri dish / agar jelly

To make an agar plate, <u>hot</u> agar jelly is poured into shallow round plastic dishes called <u>Petri dishes</u>. When the jelly's cooled and set, <u>inoculating loops</u> (wire loops) can be used to <u>transfer</u> microorganisms to the agar jelly. Alternatively, a <u>sterile dropping pipette</u> and <u>spreader</u> can be used to get an <u>even covering</u> of bacteria. The microorganisms then <u>multiply</u>.

4) In the lab at <u>school</u>, cultures of microorganisms are <u>kept at about 25 °C</u> because <u>harmful pathogens</u> are less likely to grow at this temperature. <u>Outside</u> of schools, scientists may culture microorganisms at <u>higher temperatures</u> to provide <u>optimum conditions</u> for <u>growth</u>.

You Need to Use Aseptic Techniques When Growing Bacteria

<u>Contamination</u> by <u>unwanted</u> microorganisms will <u>affect your results</u> and can potentially result in the growth of <u>pathogens</u>. To <u>avoid</u> this, the following <u>aseptic techniques</u> should be used:

1) The Petri dishes and growth medium must be <u>sterilised</u> before use. This can be done by placing them in a machine called an <u>autoclave</u>, which uses <u>steam</u> at a <u>high pressure</u> and <u>temperature</u> to <u>kill</u> any microorganisms present.

2) Before being used to transfer bacteria, an <u>inoculating loop</u> should be <u>sterilised</u> by <u>passing it through a hot flame</u>, so that any <u>unwanted microorganisms</u> are killed.

inoculating loop

3) Liquid bacterial cultures should be kept in a <u>culture vial</u> with a <u>lid</u>. The lid should only be removed <u>briefly</u> when transferring the bacteria, to prevent <u>other microbes</u> getting in.

4) After transferring bacteria to it, a <u>Petri dish</u> should be <u>covered</u> with a lid, which should be <u>lightly taped on</u>. This is to stop microorganisms from the <u>air</u> getting in.

storing a Petri dish

5) The Petri dish should be stored <u>upside down</u> to <u>stop</u> drops of <u>condensation</u> falling onto the agar.

Experimentus apparatus...

Wizardry won't help you here, unfortunately. It's best you just get your head down and learn this stuff.

PRACTICAL | Safety, Ethics and Heating

Experiments can be <u>fun</u> but they can also be <u>risky</u> — you need your <u>grown-up hat on</u> when doing practicals.

Make Sure You're Working Safely in the Lab

1) <u>Before</u> you start any experiment, make sure you know about any <u>safety precautions</u> to do with your <u>method</u> or the <u>chemicals</u> you're using. You need to <u>follow</u> any instructions that your teacher gives you <u>carefully</u>. The chemicals you're using may be <u>hazardous</u> — for example, they might be <u>flammable</u> (<u>catch fire easily</u>), or they might <u>irritate</u> or <u>burn</u> your <u>skin</u> if it comes into contact with them.

2) Make sure that you're wearing <u>sensible clothing</u> when you're in the lab (e.g. open shoes won't protect your feet from spillages). When you're doing an experiment, you should wear a <u>lab coat</u> to protect your skin and clothing. Depending on the experiment, you may need to also wear <u>safety goggles</u> and <u>gloves</u>.

3) You also need to be aware of <u>general safety</u> in the lab, e.g. keep anything <u>flammable</u> away from lit Bunsen burners, don't directly touch any <u>hot equipment</u>, handle <u>glassware</u> (e.g. test tubes, boiling tubes, beakers and microscope slides) carefully to <u>avoid breakages</u>, etc.

You Need to Think About Ethical Issues In Your Experiments

Any <u>organisms</u> involved in your investigations need to be treated <u>safely</u> and <u>ethically</u>. <u>Animals</u> need to be treated <u>humanely</u> — they should be <u>handled carefully</u> and any wild animals captured for studying should be <u>returned to their original habitat</u>. Any animals kept in the lab should also be <u>cared for</u> in a humane way, e.g. they should not be kept in conditions that are <u>too hot</u>. If you are carrying out an experiment involving other <u>students</u>, they should not be forced to participate <u>against their will</u> or feel <u>pressured</u> to take part.

Bunsen Burners Have a Naked Flame

Bunsen burners are good for <u>heating things quickly</u>. But you need to make sure you're using them <u>safely</u>:

- You should always use a Bunsen burner on a <u>heat-proof mat</u>.
- If your Bunsen burner is alight but not heating anything, make sure you <u>close</u> the hole so that the flame becomes <u>yellow</u> and <u>clearly visible</u>.
- Use the <u>blue</u> flame to heat things. If you're heating a vessel <u>in</u> the flame, hold it at the <u>top</u> (e.g. with <u>tongs</u>) and point the opening <u>away from</u> yourself (and others).
- If you're heating something <u>over</u> the flame (e.g. a beaker of water), you should put a <u>tripod and gauze</u> over the Bunsen burner before you light it, and place the vessel on this.
- Whenever you use a Bunsen burner, you should wear <u>safety goggles</u> to protect your eyes.

Heat-proof mat

Hole is closed

to gas

The Temperature of an Electric Water Bath Can Be Set

1) A <u>water bath</u> is a container filled with water that can be heated to a <u>specific temperature</u>. A <u>simple</u> water bath can be made by heating a <u>beaker of water</u> over a <u>Bunsen burner</u> and monitoring the temperature with a <u>thermometer</u> (see p.72). However, it can be hard to keep the temperature of the water <u>constant</u>.

2) An <u>electric water bath</u> will <u>monitor</u> and <u>adjust</u> the temperature for you. It's a much easier way of keeping the temperature of a reaction mixture constant. Here's how you use one:

- <u>Set</u> the temperature on the water bath, and allow the water to <u>heat up</u>.
- To make sure it's reached the right temperature, use a <u>thermometer</u>.
- Place the vessel containing your substance in the water bath using <u>test tube holders</u> or <u>tongs</u>. The level of the water outside the vessel should be <u>just above</u> the level of the substance inside the vessel.
- The substance will then be warmed to the <u>same temperature</u> as the water. As the substance in the vessel is surrounded by water, the heating is very <u>even</u>.

water bath
rack
vessel
temperature display
temperature control

Naked flames — ooo er...

Working safely and ethically is a really big part of carrying out an experiment. You need to be thinking about these things before you so much as pick up a test tube, or cut up a plant.

Sampling

I love samples... especially when I'm a bit peckish in the supermarket and they're handing out free cheese. Unfortunately, this page isn't about those samples. It's a lot more useful than that...

Sampling Should be Random

1) When you're investigating a population, it's generally not possible to study every single organism in the population. This means that you need to take samples of the population you're interested in.

2) The sample data will be used to draw conclusions about the whole population, so it's important that it accurately represents the whole population.

3) To make sure a sample represents the population, it should be random.

Page 59 tells you how data collected from samples can be used to estimate population size.

Organisms Should Be Sampled At Random Sites in an Area

1) If you're interested in the distribution of an organism in an area, or its population size, you can take population samples in the area using quadrats, pitfall traps or transects (see pages 59-60).

2) If you only take samples from one part of the area, your results will be biased — they may not give an accurate representation of the whole area.

3) To make sure that your sampling isn't biased, you need to use a method of choosing sampling sites in which every site has an equal chance of being chosen. For example:

If you're looking at plant species in a field...

1) 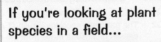Divide the field into a grid.

2) Label the grid along the bottom and up the side with numbers.

3) Use a random number generator (on a computer or calculator) to select coordinates, e.g. (2,6).

4) Take your samples at these coordinates.

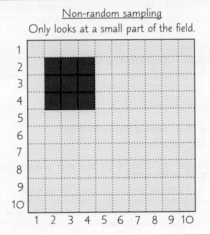

Non-random sampling
Only looks at a small part of the field.

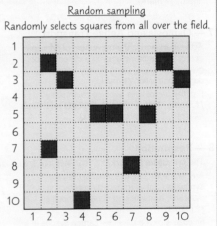

Random sampling
Randomly selects squares from all over the field.

Sampling Methods Have Limitations

Sampling techniques aren't perfect — you need to be aware of some of the limitations and sources of error you might come across when using quadrats or pitfall traps. For example:

- Collecting data using quadrats or pitfall traps can take ages — the number of samples you can collect will be limited by the time you have available.

- Only certain species can be sampled — e.g. if you want to sample large plants or flying insects then quadrats and pitfall traps won't be much good.

- In pitfall traps, organisms could be eaten by other organisms in the trap before you count them.

- Sampling often involves a degree of human judgement — e.g. to decide whether or not you count organisms that aren't fully in the quadrat or to identify the organisms that you find. Too many errors or inconsistencies in human judgement can lead to your results being invalid.

These limitations and sources of error mean that if your data is scaled up (e.g. to estimate population size) then the results may not be accurate. You might need to talk about limitations and sources of error if you're evaluating sampling methods, e.g. say how they may have affected the results and how they could be avoided.

'Eeny, meeny, miny, moe' just doesn't cut it any more...

Sampling is an important part of an investigation. It needs to be done randomly, or the data won't be worth much.

Answers

Section 1a — Cells and Respiration

p.13 — Cell Structure
Q1 a) Contains genetic material that controls the activities of the cell *[1 mark]*.
b) Where most of the reactions for respiration take place *[1 mark]*.
c) Involved in the synthesis of proteins *[1 mark]*.

p.14 — Cells and Microscopes
Q1 Place a drop of mountant/water on the slide *[1 mark]*. Use tweezers to place the specimen on the mountant/water *[1 mark]*. Add a drop of stain *[1 mark]*. Carefully apply a cover slip over the specimen *[1 mark]*.

p.15 — Calculating Cell Size
Q1 Approximately three cells in 0.6 mm
$0.6 \times 1000 = 600$ μm
$600 \div 3 = 200$ μm *[2 marks for correct answer, otherwise 1 mark for correct working]*

p.16 — Diffusion
Q1 During diffusion substances move across a cell membrane by travelling down their concentration gradient *[1 mark]* without using energy *[1 mark]*.

p.17 — Osmosis and Active Transport
Q1 Active transport is the movement of particles across a membrane against a concentration gradient *[1 mark]* using energy transferred during respiration *[1 mark]*.
Q2 E.g. the carrot cells become plasmolysed *[1 mark]*. This is because the cells lose water as a result of osmosis *[1 mark]*.

p.18 — Respiration
Q1 The cytoplasm *[1 mark]*.
Q2 Any two from: e.g. cell division / protein synthesis / active transport / contracting muscles / transmission of nerve impulses. *[2 marks]*
Q3 glucose + oxygen ⟶ carbon dioxide + water + energy *[1 mark for correct words before the arrow, 1 mark for correct words after the arrow]*

p.19 — More on Respiration
Q1 Ethanol and carbon dioxide *[1 mark]*.

p.20 — Investigating Respiration
Q1 a) E.g. a test tube with glass beads that are the same mass as the germinating beans *[1 mark]*. (You could use boiled beans instead of glass beads.)
b) A series of water baths each set to a different temperature *[1 mark]*.

Section 1b — DNA and Proteins

p.22 — DNA and Genes
Q1 thymine/T *[1 mark]*
Q2 A small section of DNA found on a chromosome *[1 mark]* that codes for a specific protein *[1 mark]*.

p.23 — Protein Synthesis
Q1 mRNA carries a complementary copy of the genetic code *[1 mark]* from the DNA in the nucleus to the ribosome in the cytoplasm *[1 mark]*.

p.24 — Enzymes
Q1 If the pH is too high or too low, it can interfere with the bonds holding the enzyme together. This changes the shape of the active site *[1 mark]* and denatures the enzyme *[1 mark]*.

p.25 — Investigating Enzyme Activity
Q1 Any two from: e.g. the pH of the reaction mixture / the volume of hydrogen peroxide used / the concentration of hydrogen peroxide used / the type of potato used / the size of the potato cube used *[2 marks]*.

p.26 — Genetic Engineering
Q1 They are used to transfer a gene from one organism into a bacterial cell/another organism *[1 mark]*.

Section 2a — Reproduction

p.28 — Mitosis
Q1 E.g. growth *[1 mark]*, replacement of damaged cells *[1 mark]*.

p.29 — Cell Specialisation and Stem Cells
Q1 E.g. tissue stem cells are not as versatile as embryonic stem cells. / Tissue stem cells cannot differentiate into all cell types, unlike embryonic stem cells. *[1 mark]*

p.30 — Cell Organisation
Q1 That it is made up of different tissues *[1 mark]* that work together to perform a particular function *[1 mark]*.

p.31 — Sexual Reproduction
Q1 24 *[1 mark]*

p.32 — Variation
Q1 Discrete variation *[1 mark]* because the phenotypes in the population will be distinct / the characteristic is inherited by single gene inheritance *[1 mark]*.

p.33 — Genetic Diagrams
Q1 The organism has two recessive alleles for that characteristic *[1 mark]*.

p.34 — More on Genetic Diagrams
Q1 a) Ff and ff *[1 mark]*.
b)

		John's gametes	
		F	F
Susan's gametes	F	FF	FF
	f	Ff	Ff

Predicted phenotype ratio —
unaffected : carrier : disorder = 2 : 2 : 0
= 1 : 1 : 0
[1 mark for correctly identifying John and Susan's gametes, 1 mark for correctly completing a Punnett square, 1 mark for the correct phenotype ratio of the offspring]
c) E.g. because the gametes that combined during fertilisation to produce John and Susan's offspring were determined by a completely random process *[1 mark]*.

Section 2b — Control and Communication

p.36 — The Nervous System
Q1 It is responsible for muscle coordination *[1 mark]*.

p.37 — Neurons and Synapses
Q1 receptor cells *[1 mark]*
Q2 motor neurons *[1 mark]*
Q3 Chemicals/neurotransmitters diffuse across the synapse between the neurons *[1 mark]*. These set off a new electrical signal in the next neuron *[1 mark]*.

p.38 — Reflexes
Q1 a) A muscle in the chef's arm *[1 mark]*.
b) In the spinal cord. / In an unconscious part of the brain. *[1 mark]*

p.39 — The Endocrine System
Q1 In the blood *[1 mark]*.
Q2 A gland which produces (and releases) hormones *[1 mark]*.

p.40 — Controlling Blood Glucose
Q1 The pancreas *[1 mark]*.
Q2 The pancreas secretes insulin *[1 mark]*. Insulin causes glucose to move from the blood into liver and muscle cells *[1 mark]*. In these cells, glucose is turned into glycogen for storage *[1 mark]*.

Section 2c — Transport Systems

p.42 — The Circulatory System
Q1 the right ventricle *[1 mark]*

p.43 — The Blood Vessels
Q1 They have a big central channel to help the blood flow despite the low pressure *[1 mark]* and they have valves to keep the blood flowing in the right direction *[1 mark]*.
Q2 E.g. networks of capillaries carry blood to every cell in the body to exchange substances with them *[1 mark]*. They have permeable walls, so that substances can easily diffuse in and out of them *[1 mark]*. Their walls are usually only one cell thick, which increases the rate of diffusion *[1 mark]*. They have a large surface area, which also increases the rate of diffusion *[1 mark]*.

p.44 — The Blood
Q1 oxyhaemoglobin *[1 mark]*

p.45 — The Immune System
Q1 They engulf and digest pathogens *[1 mark]*.

p.46 — Exchanging Materials
Q1 It means that substances only have to travel a short distance *[1 mark]*.

p.47 — Plant Structure
Q1 Any two from: e.g. stems / roots / leaves *[2 marks]*.

Answers

p.48 — Transport in Plants

Q1 Phloem vessels transport sugar *[1 mark]* made in the leaves to the rest of the plant *[1 mark]*.

Q2 The lignin strengthens the xylem vessels *[1 mark]*, which allows them to withstand changes in pressure caused by water moving through them *[1 mark]*.

p.49 — Transpiration

Q1 lower leaf epidermis / the bottom surface of leaves *[1 mark]*

Q2 Water is lost from a plant's leaves by evaporation and diffusion *[1 mark]*. This creates a slight shortage of water in the leaves, so more water is drawn up through the xylem vessels to replace it *[1 mark]*. This in turn means more water is drawn up from the roots, so there's a constant movement of water / transpiration stream through the plant *[1 mark]*.

p.50 — Transpiration Rate

Q1 Any three from: e.g. surface area / temperature / wind speed / humidity *[3 marks]*.

Section 3a — Photosynthesis

p.52 — Photosynthesis

Q1 Chlorophyll traps the light energy needed for photosynthesis *[1 mark]*.

Q2 Oxygen and hydrogen *[1 mark]*.

p.53 — More on Photosynthesis

Q1 cellulose / starch *[1 mark]*

p.55 — The Rate of Photosynthesis

Q1 Any two from: e.g: light intensity / CO_2 concentration / time plant is left to photosynthesise / the species of plant used *[2 marks]*.

Section 3b — Ecosystems

p.57 — Ecosystems and Competition

Q1 The unique role an organism plays in its community *[1 mark]*.

p.58 — Abiotic and Biotic Factors

Q1 Any two from: moisture level / light intensity / temperature / pH *[2 marks]*

p.59 — Investigating Ecosystems

Q1 a) E.g. place quadrats at random sample points in the two sample areas of the field *[1 mark]*. Count all of the buttercups within the quadrats *[1 mark]*. Calculate the mean number of buttercups per quadrat for each area and compare the results *[1 mark]*.

b) e.g. pitfall traps *[1 mark]*

p.60 — More on Investigating Ecosystems

Q1 Mark out a line across the field using a tape measure *[1 mark]*. Place quadrats at intervals/ next to each other along the line *[1 mark]*. Count and record the number of individuals from the species that are found in each quadrat *[1 mark]*.

p.61 — Investigating Factors Affecting Distribution

Q1 e.g. a light meter *[1 mark]*

p.62 — Food Chains and Food Webs

Q1 A larger mice population may reduce the amount of wheat available to the aphids, so the number of aphids may decrease *[1 mark]*. This would mean that there is less food available to the ladybirds, so their population size could decrease *[1 mark]*.

p.63 — Energy in Ecosystems

Q1 B, because the bar for the producer is smaller than for the primary consumer *[1 mark]* and just one tree/large plant may feed many consumers *[1 mark]*.

p.64 — Increasing Crop Yields — Pesticides

Q1 a) Mean yield = (30 + 28 + 32 + 34) ÷ 4
= 31 tonnes per hectare *[1 mark]*.

b) E.g. sprayed pesticide/insecticide on his potato plants *[1 mark]*. Used a biological control such as a predator of the beetle / an organism that causes disease in beetles *[1 mark]*.

p.65 — Increasing Crop Yields — Fertilisers

Q1 a) They take them up from water in the soil *[1 mark]*.

b) To make amino acids *[1 mark]*, which are used for protein synthesis *[1 mark]*.

p.66 — Increasing Crop Yields — GM Crops

Q1 E.g. to be resistant to insects *[1 mark]*, to be resistant to herbicides *[1 mark]* and to require less fertiliser *[1 mark]*.

Section 3c — Evolution

p.68 — Mutations

Q1 A mutation that has no effect on an organism's phenotype *[1 mark]*.

p.69 — Natural Selection

Q1 Some of the musk oxen may have had an allele which gave them thicker fur *[1 mark]*. These oxen would have been more likely to survive and reproduce *[1 mark]* and so pass on the allele for thicker fur *[1 mark]*. This process of natural selection may have continued over many generations, until all the musk oxen had thick fur *[1 mark]*.

p.70 — Speciation

Q1 E.g. salinity, pH and different habitats *[3 marks]*.

Index

BZR41